₽PLOUGHSHARES

Summer 2018 • Vol. 44, No. 2

GUEST EDITOR
Jill McCorkle

EDITOR-IN-CHIEF
Ladette Randolph

MANAGING EDITOR
Ellen Duffer

POETRY EDITOR
John Skoyles

PRODUCTION MANAGER
Allison Trujillo

SENIOR EDITORIAL ASSISTANT
Palak Patel

BUSINESS & CIRC. MANAGER
Cory Bailey

EDITORIAL ASSISTANTS
Dana Alsamsam & Colleen Risavy

MARKETING ASSOCIATE
Alyssa Loebig

OPERATIONS ASSISTANT
Kira Venturini

MARKETING ASSISTANT
Rebecca Angelides

COPY EDITOR
Carol Farash

SENIOR READERS
Sarah Banse, Nora Caplan-Bricker,
Karen Lonzo, John Allen Taylor,
& Jaime Zuckerman

BLOG EDITOR
Ellen Duffer

ASSOCIATE BLOG EDITOR
Amelia Hassani

LOOK2 EDITOR
David Weinstein

INTERNS
Catherine Bai, Cassandra Martinez, Harini Rajagopalan,
Brittany Shear, & Anna Sudderth

READERS
Jana-Lee Balish | Holli Carrell | Stephanie Cohen | Zachary Doss
Hannah Dow | Andrew Dugan | Maggie Ferguson | Derek Heckman
Joshua Johnson | Caroline McCoy | Autumn McClintock | Lara
Palmqvist | Suzanne Reeder | Brandi Reissenweber | David Sanchez
Michael Schrimper | Jordan Stillman | Maggie Su | Morgan Thomas

ADVISORY BOARD
DeWitt Henry | Alice Hoffman | Jill Ellen Karp | Ann Leary
Helen Elaine Lee | Pamela Painter | Tom Perrotta | Janet Silver
Marillyn Zacharis

Ploughshares, a journal of new writing, is guest-edited serially by prominent writers who explore different personal visions, aesthetics, and literary circles. Ploughshares is published in January, April, July, and October at Emerson College: 120 Boylston Street, Boston, MA 02116-4624. Telephone: (617) 824-3757. Web address: pshares.org. Email: pshares@pshares.org.

Subscriptions (ISSN 0048-4474): $35 for one year (4 issues), $55 for two years (8 issues), and $70 for three years (12 issues); $50 a year for institutions. Add $35 a year for international postage ($15 for Canada and Mexico).

Upcoming: Fall 2018, a longform prose issue edited by Ladette Randolph, will be published in October 2018. Winter 2018-19, a staff-edited poetry and prose issue, will be published in January 2019. Spring 2019, a poetry and prose issue edited by Rigoberto González, will be published in April 2019. Summer 2019, a prose issue edited by Viet Thanh Nguyen, will be published in July 2019.

Submissions: The regular reading period is from June 1 to January 15 (postmark and online dates). All submissions sent from January 16 to May 31 will be returned unread. From March 1 to May 15, we read for our Emerging Writer's Contest. Please see page 194 for editorial and submission policies, or visit our website: pshares.org/submit.

Donate: Ploughshares greatly appreciates the support of its patrons. To give your tax-deductible contribution to the Ploughshares Endowed Fund, call us at (617) 824-3753 or visit www.pshares.org/engage/donate.

Back-issue, classroom-adoption, and bulk orders may be placed directly through Ploughshares. Ploughshares is also available as full-text products from EBSCO, H.W. Wilson, JSTOR, ProQuest, and the Gale Group, and indexed in Humanities International Index and Book Review Index. The views and opinions expressed in this journal are solely those of the authors. All rights for individual works revert to the authors upon publication. Ploughshares receives support from the Massachusetts Cultural Council.

Retail distribution by TNG Specialty, Media Solutions, Ubiquity, and Disticor Direct in Canada. Printed in the U.S.A. by The Journeyman Press.

Cover art: David Pohl, *Design for Living*.

© 2018 by Emerson College. ISBN 978-1-62608-143-7
ISSN 0048-4474

HONORIFIC

PLOUGHSHARES PATRONS

This nonprofit publication would not be possible without the support of our readers and the generosity of the following individuals and organizations.

EDITOR'S CIRCLE ($10,000+)
The Green Angel Foundation ‡
Marillyn Zacharis, in memory of
Robert E. Courtemanche ‡
Hunter C. Bourne III†
Timothy Carey*

PUBLISHERS ($5,000+)
Jan and Jeff Greenhawt*
Denis and Ann Leary*
Jill Karp

COUNCIL ($3,500+)
Lauren Groff

PATRONS ($1,000+)
Alice Byers ‡
Joan Parrish †
Craig Donegan*
Elizabeth R. Rea of the Dungannon
Foundation*
Carol Davis
Tisa Jackson
Lee Pelton
Tom Perrotta

ADVOCATES ($500+)
Alan Bowers
Patricia and Paul Buddenhagen
Michael and Lynne MacWade
Newbury Owner LLC

FRIENDS ($250+)
James Carroll and Alexandra
Marshall †
James Tilley †
Sandra Leong*
Hugh Coyle and Maynard Yost
Kathleen Hill
Irving House at Harvard

READERS ($125+)
Edward H. Cardoza Jr. ‡
John Donner ‡
Kristen Kish †
Deborah B. Davis*
Andrea Barrett
Davis Enloe
Joshua Ferris
Teresa Frederick
Erin Keogh
Peter Levitt
Erich Meager
Timothy Oliveri
Omolola Ogunyemi
Pamela Painter
Robin Politan
Tim Suermondt
Ariele Taylor
Rolf Yngve

OTHER DONORS
Stephanie Kaplan Cohen †
James P. Higgins †
Eileen Pollack*
Steven Schwartz*

ORGANIZATIONS
Emerson College ‡
Massachusetts Cultural Council ‡
National Endowment for the Arts ‡

CONSECUTIVE YEARS OF GIVING:
* denotes three consecutive years of giving
† denotes five consecutive years of giving
‡ denotes ten or more consecutive years of
giving

CONTENTS

Summer 2018

JILL McCORKLE
Introduction

There are many things I look for in a story—a vivid character or place, a memorable situation, a new way of seeing something. I like to be pulled in for a ride where I'm not quite sure where I'm going but feel confident that the driver *does* know and will indeed deliver me to the right place. I find that some of the most satisfying moments in fiction are those where I might gasp with shock or surprise only to immediately see that I should have known, that indeed there is a carefully scattered path of bread crumbs that led me there. To find surprise and logic in the same moment is a feat I greatly admire. Sometimes it grows out of physical forces and action and other times it is simply a quiet shift in awareness. Either way, the world is forever changed for those at the center of it and there is a kind of emotional truth to which we, the reader, respond.

I'm drawn to humor, especially those fragments that might spring from the darkest cracks. What is happening might not be funny, but the dialogue or description is. There is the desire to laugh in spite of a serious situation; sometimes it's a deflection for the character avoiding the dark side, and sometimes it grows out of irony, highlighting innocence or ignorance, and sometimes it is simply the way a character views the world, but the result is finding yourself perched there between wanting to laugh and wanting to cry. The marriage of tragedy and comedy is not unlike that of surprise and logic; it often wakes us up and shines a light on what is most vulnerable.

I think this is why I love the voices of children and adolescents; children are immediately victims of whatever adult world they are born into and there is an emotional honesty that can't help but come into play. My very first writing teacher, Max Steele, once told our class that we would never be the writers we were meant to be until we had dealt with our mother issues. I heard this as an eighteen-year-old and it is something I have thought about ever since. In fact, in my own writing classes, I refer to it as: *if it's not one thing, it's your mother* and have been both surprised and delighted over the years to see how often a character's mother, or the absent mother, ends up being the key to whatever is missing.

I was delighted in my reading for Ploughshares to discover all of the above. There are vivid characters and places and there are those wonderful moments of illumination. There are memorable young voices looking for ways over or through the walls that define their worlds and there are mothers (and fathers) looking at it from the angle of parenthood. I did not come to the table with a thematic agenda at all, but it is uncanny how works put on the table together will often strike up a kind of dialogue. I've taught for over thirty years now and am always amazed at how often the workshop stories have common variables—sometimes the connection is as obvious as a plot line or obvious theme, and other times it is something subtle, like a reference to a place or a particular time or maybe both characters have cats or mothers who have cats; whatever they share is often worth mentioning just for the sake of conversation, sometimes providing a natural call and response to a larger theme or recognition. Then it is impossible not to step back and see the greater context of it all—the Zeitgeist.

Needless to say, the ghosts of our time are hovering close and references to the varying roles of women's lives are present as are racial tensions and class divides. Likewise, the role of man is examined; there is reference to *the wounded man* of Paleolithic cave art, and I was struck by the many ways men are wounded: in nature while struggling to survive as in the ancient painting, and then emotionally through love and loss, physically at the hands of another human, and psychologically when bred on rigid ideas or prejudice, hatred, and the desire to inflict wounds on others.

This collection is one of prose—amazing essays and short stories— but along the way, I was fortunate enough to receive some poems from Wendell Berry, which are also included. The titles themselves could serve as road signs for what is within this volume: *The Muse, Composition, Service, And Where are You?* And then there's the one that I think needs to be on billboards everywhere: *Old Man, Dead Rooster,* a poem that speaks to the *haves* and *have nots.* A good story, after all, thrives on what is missing and being sought: freedom, salvation, acceptance, understanding, a simple answer or possession or new way of seeing. Will they find it? Will they get there? *That's* a story to be told, and there are many wonderful ones up ahead that I hope the reader will appreciate as much as I have.

BELLE BOGGS
In the Shadow of Man

Ben was late for school pickup; Wednesday was Diana's day, but he'd forgotten that she had a meeting at the university until she texted him just after 3:00. When he picked Olivia up on time, he had to wait in a long line of cars until one of the teachers checked his dashboard sign, then walkie-talkied inside to summon his daughter. On accidental late days like this—about once a week, no matter who was doing pickup— he parked in the small paved lot and walked inside to find her hula- hooping or coloring or helping her teacher, Ms. Susan, sort math manipulatives or clean the old-fashioned chalkboards.

They were lucky to have gotten into Sunshine Charter, Diana reminded Ben when he complained about the lack of bus service or school lunches. "The Free Friends," some of the other parents called it before praising the school's philosophy of project-based learning, the copious time outside, the fact that homework was forbidden— forbidden! A lottery system with sibling preference and a wait list a hundred kids deep—what were the chances? Ms. Susan, who'd come down South from Brooklyn, as she often reminded people, was more traditional than some of the other teachers, sneaking in worksheets and occasional math homework and insisting on the respectful (and hierarchical, some parents felt) *Ms.*, but Ben liked her no-nonsense attitude and strict control over the class. Some of the other classes, Olivia said, could be a little wild.

Diana, who taught evolutionary biology at Duke, liked the field trips, and this was Olivia's favorite part of school too. So far this year they'd been to all the free local museums, plus the water treatment plant, an artist's studio, a welding shop, and a biodiesel plant—and it was only October. The field was where real learning happened, Diana maintained, though it had been some years since she'd been to the African preserve where the baboons she studied lived.

Olivia had asked him to chaperone the one today—please, Daddy?— but Ben, who was on furlough from his own government job, had a networking event to attend.

"Not back yet," Ms. Susan told him as he entered the classroom. Ben was relieved—no admonishments from Olivia—until he saw two other parents seated grumpily at the small desks. What were their names? Margaret, he thought, mother of Declan? And someone else's dad, in heavy steel toe work boots, scrolling on his phone.

"Can you call again?" asked Margaret, standing up and hooking her purse over her shoulder, like her own readiness might be convincing. "Can I call? We have a game soon."

"I'm sure they'll be here any minute," Ms. Susan said. She was seated placidly at her desk, working through a pile of notebooks—the journals the third-graders kept for recording observations about nature. Squirrel Studies, Olivia called her notebook, Ben remembered. He felt a sudden possessiveness, the desire to have his child back.

"It's Todd who's driving," Margaret told him, with a significant look. "Todd Dougherty. He and Lori are divorcing." She ticked off the kids in the car: "He's got his daughter Lizzie, Olivia, Luis, and Declan."

"It happens sometimes," Ms. Susan said, turning pages and applying stamps and stickers. Last year's teacher, who just went by Amy, never used stickers but instead wrote notes in colored pencil that neither praised nor criticized, only made observations. *You are paying a lot of attention to color*, one might read. Or, *It rains a lot in spring*. Olivia liked the stickers, some of them featuring the Disney princesses forbidden by the handbook.

"Divorce ain't a crime," Ms. Susan continued, almost as if she were talking to herself. "If it was, half this school would be in jail." Ben found her saltiness reassuring—a reminder that the keyed-up anxieties that came with a certain brand of modern parenting were a waste of energy. A reminder that the kids would be fine, no matter what bullshit their parents or the world exposed them to. She looked up and said, in a softer tone, "He probably took them for ice cream and lost track of time."

"Declan is *vegan*."

"*Sorbet*," Ms. Susan said. "I'll call them again in a minute. Why don't you go downstairs and look around the gallery wall? The kids just finished a big project in art class."

"But when—"

"The Year 2030," Ben announced. Margaret looked at him with such distress that he quickly clarified: "The art project. That's what it was about. The kids imagining life in the year 2030."

"Oh," she said. "That does sound interesting." She followed him out the door.

The gallery was nothing more than a dimly lit hallway on the school's first floor, with a strip of corkboard used to display the kids' work, hung a little lower than an adult's eye level. The art teacher was in a band that toured each summer in Europe, stateside during the school year, and had full tattoo sleeves that made Ben's own bare arms feel a little naked. Everyone's bio at the school, it seemed, had something interesting attached to it, some complexity that suggested that the work of teaching was just one of a vast array of interesting vocations that could occupy their time. The kids could go weeks without an art class, but Ben had to admit that the projects were well-done, far more elaborate and interdisciplinary—a major code-word for the teachers—than the color wheels and still lifes he remembered from his own years in elementary school.

THE YEAR 2030: CHALLENGES AHEAD, read an ominous sign at the start of the hall.

"Declan will be twenty-two," said Margaret. "Graduating from college. And I'll be..." She started counting on her fingers, then trailed off. "Old."

"And itchy, apparently," said Ben, nodding at the first poster. POISON IVY WILL OVERRUN WILD SPACES, the poster claimed in green bubble letters. The tempera-painted leaves-of-three trailed off the poster's edges in a way that suggested invasiveness, and the student listed the reasons for her prediction at the poster's base: deforestation, climate change, biodiversity loss.

"Not swimming in the ocean," said Margaret, pointing at the next one: JELLYFISH CLOG OUR WATERS. A SEA OF STINGERS. OUCH!

Ben walked down the hall, scanning posters. He realized, despite his own work as a water quality specialist for the state—a furloughed water quality specialist—that he was hoping for good news.

ZIKA IS COMING. EVEN MORE HORRIBLE DISEASES. MOSQUITOES WILL LOVE IT IN 2030.

It will be easy to get a tan, read a cheerful-looking poster painted with a bright orange sun. AND CANCER.

"Here's Olivia's," said Margaret, peering at a small, neatly lettered poster. "Clever. It's scratch-and-sniff."

"I wouldn't," Ben warned. Olivia had based her project on some of the work that he had been doing before his furlough, about pollution in the state's chicken and pig farming regions. She'd mixed up a noxious concoction in the kitchen, using moldy fridge scraps and essential oils, and painted it onto strips of fine-gauge sandpaper. She'd chosen the title of her project herself—FOWL SMELLS—and translated it into Spanish.

"I worry about these kids," he said, partly as a way of deflecting the anxieties he knew Olivia's detailed poster, with its puns, graphs, and tables, would provoke—not about chicken waste, but about the other kids' invented spelling, clumsy lettering, and monolingualism. "All this doom and gloom. They'll have ulcers before they're in middle school. There's probably a poster about that somewhere."

"I find their passion inspiring," Margaret said. Declan's poster was noticeably missing. She checked her watch. "But this thing with the field trips—it makes me nervous. What happened to buses? And head counts?"

"I'm sure they'll be back any minute," Ben assured her. But privately he agreed. The system was unbelievable to him—parents and teachers, driving their own cars as chaperones, stood in the school's commons and held up fingers to indicate the number of free spaces that remained in their vehicles as students raced around with their friends, musical chairs–style. The object was not to have to ride with the principal, Olivia told her parents—Tamara listened avidly to books on tape, which you were not allowed to interrupt by talking above a whisper, and did not allow eating or even gum chewing in her station wagon. The best was to ride with a smoker—anything goes with a smoker, Olivia believed. Does someone write down who goes in what car? he'd asked, exasperated. Olivia had shrugged. It's not hard to remember

Diana called the system ingenious—it made field trips free, or almost free, and easier for teachers to schedule—but Ben thought that her years studying and working in developing countries had made her somewhat blind to basic safety issues. He sometimes thought Diana led a charmed life, with her smooth path to tenure, the comfortable mix of public and private grants that funded her research, the legions of devoted student acolytes, eager to do anything she asked. She wore no makeup (she didn't need it), ate only when she was hungry, and woke every day at 6:30, with no alarm.

Of course she worked hard and made sacrifices—she'd lived for more than a year in a minimally equipped tent in the Amboseli National Park, and now was more often in the business of dispatching graduate students and managing their research from her lab, which she found far more oppressive than the African savannah. But still: her work mattered. It would last. It was not subject to the whims of anti-environmental state legislators who tracked her every email.

He was wondering if he should call her now, to tell her about the missing car of students, when they heard the school's front door open.

"They must be here," said Margaret. "Finally."

They walked rather quickly through the exhibit space and then the commons, a maze of backpacks and lunch bags dropped by the school's after-care kids. Those kids were playing outside, and Ben knew that Olivia, an only child, would ask him if she could stay a while and play with them. He'd say yes, he decided, even though he had a complicated chicken stew in mind for dinner. Screw it: they'd have pasta instead. Maybe Declan and Luis would stay too—maybe they all had ice cream, or a funny story to tell.

But it was only Tamara, back from some errand. She carried in grocery bags—did she look worried?—and waved to them from her windowed office, cell phone clutched to her ear. Luis' dad had come downstairs from the classroom and was waiting on the bench by the entrance, hand-painted by the kids to read *welcome* in charmingly crooked yellow letters, outlined in green. He was texting someone from his phone and looked even unhappier than before.

"Ms. Susan left," he said, not looking up. "She had to get her own kid from the high school." He finished his text and looked at Margaret. "What did you say about Todd?"

"I heard," Margaret began, but then her eyes filled with tears. "You know, you hear about these *disgruntled* dads, on the news…"

Tamara came out of her office then, smiling broadly, and greeted each of them with a practiced, energetic calm. "José, Margaret, Ben, you've had to wait a while now. Can I get you some snacks? I brought some veggie trays and hummus, some pita."

"*Hummus*?" Ben said. "Are you fortifying us for some kind of longer—where are our kids, Tamara?"

"It's been an hour," José said.

"We're in touch with Lori, who is on her way," Tamara said. She took the various clipboards and papers—invitations to volunteer for this or that, to plant flowers, to build a treehouse, or man the ham radio—off the small table next to the entrance and set them on the floor. Ben had volunteered far more often in Olivia's first year than he had this year, when he was on furlough, halfheartedly waiting to return to a job he hated. He'd spent almost a week putting together the European-style playground equipment, which mysteriously included no swings, no slide, and no instructions. If only he'd volunteered for this one thing— this field trip to where? A solar house?—he could be making chicken stew with olives in their sunny kitchen, or idly watching while Olivia and her friends created fairy houses from the playground's thick layer of cedar mulch. He had not even attended the networking event. He thought of that stew-making self, easily irritated by the lack of an ingredient, or the one who passed the volunteer table without stopping, with an envy that bordered on hatred.

Ben texted Diana: *Olivia not back from field trip yet, waiting at school.* "You haven't talked to Todd?" he asked with a steady voice. He'd already looked up the class parent phone list and sent half a dozen texts, none of them returned. *Hey Todd!* the first one read. *We're here at Sunshine. Give us a call?*

Hey man, read the last one. *Getting a little worried about you and the kids. Please call when you can.*

"Lori has been trying to make contact with Todd," Tamara said carefully, unpacking the unappetizing plastic trays of carrots and broccoli and grape tomatoes. The way she said it—make contact—made it sound like they were on the moon. "His phone is going straight to voicemail."

"I knew it," Margaret said. "When is he coming back? Where are they?"

"We have to talk to Lori," Tamara said. "Todd didn't answer Susan's calls. He didn't answer *my* calls."

"What about the police?" José said. He held up his phone, showing a long string of texts. "Luis' mother is asking where he is. If she finds out he was in trouble, and I didn't tell her—"

"Declan has a phone," Margaret announced suddenly. Ben realized she'd been gripping her own phone, wrapped in its tire-size rubber case, for the better part of the last hour. She must have been waiting for it to ring or vibrate with a text. "I pack it on field trips, for emergencies."

She admitted this rather defensively, as cell phones—along with Disney princess images and homework and adult surnames—were forbidden.

Yes, let's call him, everyone agreed, so happy with Margaret's paranoid and rule-breaking foresight. Why hadn't she called him already, Ben wondered, until Margaret explained that the emergency phone was for outgoing calls only. "I told him, emergencies only," Margaret said. "I really emphasized that."

"That's a good sign," Tamara said. "He doesn't think it's an emergency. He feels safe."

Ben had met Declan, a kid who wore a cape to school and often forgot his shoes on the way both in and out of the building, and did not feel reassured. Why hadn't Ben thought of that—an emergency cell phone? He could easily have hidden it in Olivia's backpack, and she would have known what to do with it, unlike this space cadet Declan kid.

As if she could hear Ben's unkind thoughts, Margaret burst into tears. Tamara patted her, offering her a carrot.

Ben tried to conjure Todd, a big guy with a long graying beard. He taught music lessons and tuned pianos and because of his flexible schedule was almost always on field trip duty. Maybe this was the reassuring fact—he'd had plenty of opportunity to go AWOL, and never had. He had frequent occasion to interact with and potentially even harm people in their own homes, and he was not currently wanted or in jail. But then Ben remembered something else—Todd had a menagerie of pet lizards and snakes, which he sometimes brought to school, perched on his shoulder or wrapped around his arm. Even Diana, who studied baboon asses for a living, thought that was a bad sign about a person.

Margaret cried harder.

"I think, yes, call the police," José said. "Maybe they can tell the location, because of the pings?"

"Is the phone on?" Tamara asked. Margaret shook her head. "Lori is afraid the police will make him more erratic. She'll be here"—Tamara checked her watch—"any minute."

Then suddenly it was nearly dark, all the warm October sunlight leached out of the sky. The afterschool kids had all departed, picked up by parents who complained—how stupidly they complained!—about the children's slowness, or the way they always forgot their jackets and backpacks and sports equipment. Even after they were gone, there was a collection of puffy nylon coats in the corner, and Ben walked to the pile. Was that pink one Olivia's? It was so small and familiar: the stiff arms that looked almost animated, the tiny hood. Ben stood over it, thinking he'd examine its pockets for the little collections Olivia carried: usually rocks and pebbles, but also errant Lego pieces, pen caps, acorns. He bent, lifted the coat, and saw that it was the very same one his daughter wore, but far too small, like something Olivia would have worn in kindergarten. Like something she would have molted.

"Hey, how's it going," said another dad, reaching past him. "I think that's my kid's."

Ben nodded dumbly. As the coat disappeared—the last bright thing in the room—he had the sensation of falling backwards, forever and ever, into the growing darkness. He made himself walk back to the group. Ms. Susan had returned with her son, who made quick work of the veggies and hummus until Ms. Susan shook her head at him. They both sat on folding chairs near the door, solemnly doing homework.

Luis' mom, Carmen, was next to Margaret on the welcome bench, holding her hand. José had left to take care of their other children—two of them, still at home—but he would be back once they'd been fed their dinner, back to collect Luis and Carmen. "Or else," he'd said, looking darkly at Tamara. Then his look crumbled into something helpless. "Or else I don't know what." But he'd nodded in a determined way at Ben, just before he left—they'd decided that José would drive to Todd and Lori's house to look around, and then back to the solar house. Ben offered to go himself—he didn't have other kids at home, after all—but José said it was better for him to be there, in case the police arrived. José had a cousin who could watch his kids, and some neighbors who could help him look.

Margaret's wife was in surgery at the hospital but would be there soon. Lori had gone to the police station, after all, and was answering questions about her husband: when they'd last talked, where he might take a carload of children.

Ben had still not called Diana, though he knew her meeting was likely over. She'd said not to expect her back until late, as she was working on a grant application and some article proofs. But she'd be there for bedtime, of course. She was reading *In the Shadow of Man* to Olivia, not an abridged version but the whole book, a fat sun-faded paperback she's owned since college, of moment-by-moment chimpanzee observation. It was a testament to how much Olivia loved this time with her mother—her clear sonorous voice, her patient explanations of difficult words and concepts, the way she let Olivia page forward to the book's few photographs—that she did not ask to switch to the newest Harry Potter, which waited on the shelf for Ben to read to her next. Diana, who spent long hours happily comparing charts detailing minute baboon behavioral changes, took Olivia's patient attention for granted.

They all took so much for granted.

He pulled up Diana's number. They had argued this morning—shouldn't he always be on pickup duty, she wondered, since he wasn't working? The way she said "wasn't working"—usually they both said *furlough*—implied some kind of choice, he said. That wasn't what she meant, it was just a true statement. Was he working today, or not? It was her dismissiveness that rankled him, though he finished packing Olivia's lunch bag without mentioning the networking event he'd later skip. This was how their arguments went: Diana too preoccupied to take note of his feelings, then silence from Ben, and she wouldn't even notice. Or maybe—and this was worse—she noticed but chose to wait for his hurt to pass.

He looked at the round icon above her number: a tiny snapshot of Diana, smiling and windblown, from Olivia's second birthday party, something they'd thrown together at a downtown park. Calling her would make the threat real, would transform Todd in a way that his mind was struggling not to, from mild-mannered music teacher to creepy reptile-obsessive. And shouldn't he be able to take care of this on his own? But he wasn't sure he was making the best moves. Already Ben's texts—sent surreptitiously from the hallway, so not to scare Margaret or upset Tamara—had gone from casual to pleading to angry.

If you touch a hair on her head...

A mistake, he realized, as soon as he pressed SEND.

He thought of Diana, her broad makeup-free face illuminated by the computer screen in her office while she innocently ate her dinner—plain yogurt, an avocado, foods that took no preparation and could be shoved into her backpack first thing—without tasting it. He thought of

José, with his heavy boots and extended-cab truck, slowly patrolling Todd and Lori's neighborhood. Should he be out searching too, instead of sending these ridiculous, unanswered texts?

Tamara's phone rang. It was Lori again. She called every ten minutes or so with an update, which Tamara related back to them: the police had Todd's plate numbers and they were notified in a seven-county range, though it would take another hour for them to declare an amber alert. She didn't *think* he would do anything harmful. It was true they'd decided to separate, but they still lived together. She'd told the police everything, everything she could think of. No amber alert, not yet— that was a relief, and it also felt cavalier.

I'm sorry man. I know you wouldn't hurt our kids. Sometimes things are tough. I just want to talk to Olivia.

He and Diana had been through their own rough patches, over the years—perhaps they were on the cusp of one now. Ben thought about writing that, how the furlough had made things hard. It wasn't even really a furlough, though that's what his department called it officially, he guessed to avoid paying a severance. It was more like a layoff, with the possibility of rehiring when the budget improved, which it probably wouldn't. And Diana had never had problems at work, which made it hard for her to understand. Maybe Todd and Lori were having issues like that—Lori a programmer, so friendly and competent, and Todd with his weird odd jobs and reptiles, his way of standing silently off to the side at school functions, arms crossed over his belly. Ben could hardly even call his voice to mind, and he knew that it was hard to feel voiceless, extraneous. But that was a lot to put in a text.

"I'm sorry," they could hear Lori saying through the crackling speakerphone, her own voice unfamiliar with fear, at the end of the call. *Just get in touch, please!* He pressed SEND again. The families had been invited to the police station, but no one wanted to leave the place where their children expected them to be. Where their children last were.

"No apologies," Tamara said to Lori. "There is only the present moment, in which we are doing everything we can."

That was the current schoolwide culture project—focusing on the present moment, and eschewing apologies or second-guessing. "You can't change the past!" Olivia was newly fond of saying, whenever Ben or Diana noticed that she'd forgotten some chore. He found this project frustrating on a regular day, but now it seemed to be an expression of everything that was wrong with the whole reckless enterprise. The past mattered. It was why he was on furlough, after meticulous research into decades-long pollution. It extended into the present, polluting the water people drank, and then into the future as they carried that pollution with them, in their bodies' very molecules.

Don't go back, Diana told him, when he first left the department. They don't deserve you. You're wasting your talent.

But Ben wasn't sure about that—sometimes he thought his talent was being married to Diana, producing—his small effort! How it paled in comparison to Diana's thirty hours of labor!—this child with her. Why had they waited so long to have her? Why didn't they have another kid, two more kids, three? Each of them smart enough to undo the damage of their presence on earth.

"I always told him," Margaret sniffed. "I told him to ride with a woman, a mom. I know that's terrible—I mean, he's a boy himself—but a woman would not do this."

"Yes," said Carmen. "Me too. I always say to Luis, you get lost and have to find a cop, find a lady cop."

"That's what my mom always told me and my brothers, in Brooklyn," Ms. Susan said. Ben could see, behind her composition journal, that she was surreptitiously grading math worksheets. "I repeated it to my own son."

"But you don't have to do that!" said Tamara. "We have taken our children on hundreds—*hundreds*—of trips, with moms and dads and teachers, women *and* men, and this has never happened before."

"I thought you only cared about the present moment," Ben said. "That's this unbelievably shitty moment, where we're waiting for the police to tell us where our kids are."

Carmen and Margaret and even Ms. Susan looked at him with such surprised approval that he continued: "If you don't care about anything but the present moment, what is that hipster art teacher doing terrorizing our kids with that nightmarish vision of the year they graduate from college?"

"You're an environmental scientist," Tamara said quietly. "You know the dangers. You are also welcome—*encouraged*—to volunteer."

"I'm looking for a job! Because I am on furlough! For however long! Because Democrats only vote in presidential years and the lunatics we did not elect think environmental quality is about fishing and hunting and making sure we can drive on the beach!" He was shouting now. "I'm sorry! I know the art teacher is right—we are well and truly fucked—but it upsets me every time I come in here."

"Ben—"

"Don't tell me not to be sorry! I have behaved inappropriately by yelling and swearing and I'm fucking sorry!"

Ms. Susan had gotten up—he thought to find some soap for washing out his mouth, or some other kind of old-fashioned punishment he would welcome—but she returned with a roll of poster board. She slowly peeled off the masking tape that held it closed.

"This is Declan's project," she said. "He wasn't finished coloring it in."

Margaret stood and shakily unrolled the poster, holding the edges as if it were a fragile artifact, an illuminated manuscript or Egyptian papyrus scroll. Across the surface of the poster, Declan had drawn and mostly crayoned in a giant green cape. "2030" was written above the top, in red letters, and in the center of the cape a large red capital S, like the Superman logo. *S is for scientist*, he'd written in a blocky mix of upper- and lowercase letters. *Scientists will be busy in 2030. Solving our problems. Making it OK to live here. So don't be scared! Stay in school!!!*

Ben didn't know what to say. Margaret wept silently and showed the poster to Carmen before rolling it up again and tenderly refastening the tape. She sat down again on the welcome bench, hugging the poster gently.

"Why don't we try a mindfulness exercise," Tamara said, motioning for them to stand. Ben could feel Ms. Susan's eyes rolling in her head, but he saw that Carmen and Margaret and even Ms. Susan and her son had followed her into the school's center hallway, where there was more room to spread out. The school had no custodians—the children were responsible for cleaning, which meant that every surface was perpetually coated in a film of grime and dust—but Tamara seated herself on the floor quite naturally, as if she did this all the time, and closed her eyes. Ben watched them from the entrance hall, and took out his phone when he saw that they had all closed their eyes.

"Picture," she said, then paused for a long moment, as if she could read, telepathically, what Ben was typing.

I will find you...

She took a deep breath and started again. "Picture something that makes you feel safe. A place. A special place where there is no fear, no judgment."

How dare you take my...

"Think of yourself in this place, the sounds you would hear..."

It was hard to keep his fingers from tapping the tiny letters, but Ben made himself stop texting. What would he think of, if he were to picture safety? What would Diana think of? He went in his mind to the center pages of Jane Goodall's book, with their black-and-white photos: chimpanzees in trees, chimpanzees in the rain, chimpanzees hugging and fighting and kissing their chimpanzee lips together. With a glittery ribbon, Olivia had bookmarked the single photo of Jane, young and slender, in the forest with her toddler son, holding him by one hand as they waded through a stream. But she never got to go back there, Olivia told Ben. After she became famous, she had to spend every moment of her life traveling to places that weren't like the Gombe forest at all. Wasn't that sad?

It was. Ben closed his eyes and pocketed his phone. He thought of the heat-shimmering Amboseli, where Diana's research station chugged on with the grad students and post-docs who sent her their research but were not her, were not as smart or capable or dedicated. He could leave his job permanently, he thought, take Olivia out of school and go there, with Diana. They could live in tents, cook over a fire, see a night sky swimming with stars. But that was impossible, Diana would say. It was not their life now.

Here was life now: a school door clanging open, the entranceway suddenly filled with the yogurt and shampoo and dirt and honey smell of children. There were Luis and Lizzie and Declan and Olivia, all of them intact and laughing and talking over each other as if their parents, sitting stunned on the grubby floor or nearly fainting—Ben didn't know he was a fainter—against the wall of Sunshine Charter, had not spent the last two hours in the worst panic and dread of their lives.

Carmen and Margaret pounced on their children first, enveloping them in hugs that swept them off their feet while Tamara made a call to Lori at the police station. Susan held the door open for Todd, who loped in, loaded with water bottles and lunch bags and backpacks. He didn't say anything, but a familiar parental exhaustion shone in his eyes. Ben placed one hand on the wall and groped the other hand toward Olivia.

"Dad," she said, ducking under his arm and hugging his side. She smelled like leaves and crayons. "We saved a turtle! A huge alligator snapper! It almost bit Todd's hand off!"

"Oh" was all that Ben could say. He looked hard at Todd, who was gently arranging the children's things near the door like some kind of large and penitent monk, matching the names on the water bottles with the names on the lunch bags. Todd straightened up and took out his phone, which Ben could see was badly cracked and taped across the front.

"I'm sorry," Todd said finally. "I thought it would only take a minute, but once we started—"

"We couldn't just leave the turtle," Luis said. "It would get hit by a car."

They took turns telling the story, how Declan had spotted the turtle in the other lane and they'd all talked Todd into pulling over. The snapper was two-and-a-half feet long! No, three feet long! And green with algae. She was trundling across the road, but so slowly. When they approached her she disappeared inside her shell, but they knew better than to pick her up.

"*We* knew better," Olivia corrected Luis. "Todd tried."

They found a strong stick and coaxed it into the snapper's mouth. She bit down and did not let go. Olivia and Lizzie each took an end and led the snapper across the road while Todd and Luis and Declan directed traffic around them. It took a while to make sure the snapper was safely in the swamp.

"And," Olivia said, "then we got lost."

"I'm sorry," Todd said. He held up his phone. "I was relying on my GPS. It ran out of battery and I don't have a car charger. I thought I'd charge it here and call Lori." He plugged it in and it came to life, then flashed and vibrated with incoming messages and texts. Ben winced at the texts he knew Todd would soon be reading from him, and probably also from Margaret and José and Tamara and even Lori, what he'd learn they thought had happened. It was no worse than what they had been through, sitting here. It was less bad because it was in the past, where you could not go. Not to change, not to fix.

"Declan," Margaret said, "why didn't you use your emergency cell?"

"My what?" Declan said. He was not wearing shoes. He did have on the cape. "Oh," he said. "Oh yeah."

"We thought—" Ben began.

"We thought something had happened—to all of you," Susan said firmly. She was handing out backpacks and graded math worksheets.

"But it didn't. We were worried, but now we're so relieved." Tamara nodded at Margaret and Ben—it was best to go now.

"Look," said Olivia, as they walked outside. It was fully dark, but under the streetlights, he could see the pastel Ariel sticker on her paper, which Ms. Susan had chosen, he knew, just for her. "I can do my sevens in under a minute."

"That's wonderful," Ben said. Really it was. It had taken him a long time, maybe until the end of middle school, to learn his sevens. He sniffed the air: sharp and clean, a fall smell. In Africa baboons and chimpanzees were trading their ancient calls. And somewhere nearer, a turtle—prehistorically armored, infinitely determined—was digging its way safely into the mud.

WENDELL BERRY

Old Man, Dead Rooster

Them that's got

got to lose.

Them that ain't

got, can't.

WENDELL BERRY

The Muse

Reach your cup into the air

and draw it back full of water.

WENDELL BERRY

Service

What I got of worldly gumption

I learned in the church of false assumption.

Under the sentence of wrath and fire

I studied the windows, the girls in the choir.

WENDELL BERRY
Composition

A small room, a small porch,

a large window, a stove,

a table, a chair, a cot,

a few books, a few thoughts,

a notebook, a pencil,

an eraser...

WENDELL BERRY

And Where are You?

Gary Snyder is a man of the West and

of the Far East, which is farther west.

Or say you go to the east, and then

you'll come first to the East, but then

to the West, which is Europe the seat

of Western Civilization. American historians

know that Kentucky once was the West

and is now the Old West, but

to Californians it is variously

the South or the East. Which is why

we Kentuckians still believe

the Earth is square and flat, and our

cardinal directions are Left and Right.

Roaming Charges

OK, it bore mention: she'd slept with the guy once, more out of politeness than anything else.

This was up in Montreal the previous winter. She and Theo Mirsky, the man who signed her paychecks, were working their way back from dinner with investors at a distinguished, much revered, but otherwise not very good brasserie near the port. They did so in companionable silence. The sidewalks were a challenge, hazardous and slick from some sort of extreme weather event earlier in the day, which, in the insulation of their fifth-floor conference room, they had apparently missed. Now the sky had cleared to a vast, blameless black. There was no available moonlight. The seagulls, as they wheeled overhead, sounded lost in the darkness, plaintive and petulant and confused. A scavenger's life was no picnic, she supposed.

Her own eyes were fixed on the cobblestones however, which were no easy trick to negotiate in four-inch heels. It didn't help that she was mildly drunk. It didn't help that she was mildly nauseous. It didn't help that over the course of the evening her distaste for the formal ambience, the heavy food, the banal conversation, and the more or less compulsory self-restraint that went along with being the only female at the table had not so much dampened her appetites as lit a fire under them, so that instead of eating and drinking less than usual she had wound up eating and drinking more. A *lot* more. Reflexively, Danielle was tempted to blame this, as she did so much of the excess and indulgence in her life, on her mother (whose biopsy results, it occurred to her now, were now three days overdue), but the connection was spurious at best; in truth she was less preoccupied with her mother that evening than she was with herself, specifically those parts of herself that happened to be desperately bored, and ravenously thirsty, and more or less completely unpreoccupied with, or for that matter even conscious of, her mother.

Anyway, she regretted it all now, on the trek back to their hotel. But then she and regret were on familiar if not promiscuous terms already. This was by no means their first assignation.

"We could call an Uber," Theo offered. "There's no shame in burning a little fossil fuel once in a while."

"I'd rather walk. I'm below my steps quota anyway."

"Fine," he said. "We'll pad our stats."

Theo was in full gallantry, aim-to-please mode. She leaned against his arm, which had been mock-formally offered on their way out of the restaurant; four blocks later she had yet to return it. She admired its impassive solidity, its tensile, gym-built strength. Give the man credit; he was nothing if not self-improving. He had applied himself industriously to the task of making his arm fit for this purpose, and it was. It seemed a lesson of sorts. All it took was a little patience, mechanized attention, and vigorous daily resistance training, and the world opened up its doors to you, submitted gratefully to your designs.

She wasn't blind to the picture the two of them presented either: a fit and handsome couple in Italian clothes, strolling arm-in-arm over the cobblestones after an expense-account dinner. She never walked this way at home with Karl. The two of them rarely so much as held hands. It would have felt off-key somehow, stagey and self-conscious, a little bogus. And yet as a girl, it occurred to her, she had often walked this way with her father. It had seemed perfectly natural back then to link arms with a grown male, a big heavy-faced gentleman in a long wool coat; to match his broad, restless strides, register his involuntary snuffles and groans, inhale his acrid animal musks. No one knew how to be adult anymore, she thought. Or was it just her? She had failed to get the memo, had fallen behind on the standards and practices, misplaced the handbooks, skipped the meetings, zoned out during the power points. Her own version of the thing, the life she'd improvised with Karl, seemed only some half-hearted parody, a fey little puppet show in which every action was subverted by indecision, every line of dialogue brutalized by air quotes, every gesture only a pantomime of a gesture, a reference to a gesture, a gesture toward a gesture...

"Ah," Theo said, "here we are."

As they pushed through the revolving doors, Theo was humming to himself, one of those tuneless and meandering compositions he liked to deploy in transitional interludes against the threat of sudden intimacy or silence. He was in an expansive mood. He'd enjoyed a few glasses of wine at dinner, enjoyed them very much indeed. Though never much of a drinker in the past, since his separation from

Eileen, he appeared to be on something of a growth curve in that area. The trends were all looking favorable. Now his hair was askew, his cheeks rowdy with blood, and his eyes as he unwound his scarf were viscous and bright, the pupils swimming tremulously in their sockets. With an air of casual expansiveness he pressed the button for the elevator and stepped back to watch the numbers obligingly reverse themselves, as he'd known of course they would. Why shouldn't they? Their meetings had gone well. Money was flowing through the pipeline; arrows of net worth inching higher; market returns soaring; end of year bonuses all but inscribing themselves on their checks. Now here they were back on Rue Sherbrooke, after a long and productive evening of hunter-gathering, sailing through the plush, overheated lobby of a five-star hotel.

Soft clouds of laughter rose from the club chairs. A tinkle of piano jazz wafted over from the bar. A merry murmur bubbled from the water element as it fell and fell from the mezzanine. It all might have been so much incidental music on the soundtrack of some urbane, beautifully constructed French-language film, Danielle thought, full of urbane, beautifully constructed French-language people who had maybe enjoyed a few drinks with dinner too, and were now mingling around, drowsy and sedate, enjoying one last round of cognacs before bed.

It was, in short, if you discounted the tedium of the dinner itself, a pleasant enough end to the evening: one of those unicorn-rare occasions where the investments of effort and dry-cleaning that had gone into business travel were earning back roughly commensurate rewards. She waited for one of them to ruin it somehow.

"How about a nightcap," Theo offered, right on cue. "I'm way too wired to sleep."

"God no. Are you kidding?"

"Now don't take an attitude," he said. "It's a perfectly innocent invitation."

"Tell you what, why don't you grab some J&B from the minibar and jerk off to pay-per-view porn instead? That's a perfectly innocent invitation too."

Theo pursed his lips, considering the proposition with his usual maddening judiciousness. "Is that what you're going to do?"

"Maybe. I don't know. Anyway," she remembered to add, "it's none of your business."

"Sheesh, I'm just kidding, Danny. Lighten up."

"I *am* light," she protested. "I'm, like, one of the lightest people I know."

In the wake of this untruth she stood there frowning and worrying the beads of her necklace, her own neurotic little catechism, waiting to be punished. It occurred to her she might have overreacted a little just now. Malign harassments were in the news, micro-aggressions and manipulations clogging up the feeds; perhaps she had been too sensitive, either misread Theo's subtext or worse, projected some worrisome, borderline ludicrous subtext of her own. God knows Danielle was not at her most lucid at that point. Her nerves felt gloopy, unstrung. Chimes of midnight were bonging in her temples, tolling some mournful message she could not quite get it together to decode. How much had she drunk? Though the data on this wasn't readily available in her mind (somewhere between the appetizers and main course she'd lost count of how many times her glass was refilled by one overly attentive gentleman or another), it was, she knew, all too accessible on her phone, where her Alc-Calc Pro had been issuing a series of cheerful *pings* all evening, charting every wayward spike of her blood alcohol content, every errant leap over her absorption-and-metabolism baselines. No doubt she'd sailed way past her benchmarks on the Château Greysac alone, and that wasn't even taking into account the Negronis beforehand, the Armagnacs after, and the benzodiazepines she'd downed on the sly, more or less prophylactically, in the cab on the way to the restaurant. They were all still with her now. In her puffy hooded parka she felt gassy and bloated, an unmoored dirigible drifting toward an invisible power line. Everything was moving in slow, sickly, gelatinous motion. The sealike undulations of the carpet, the halos revolving around the chandeliers, the teasing, tortuous descent of the elevator, like an angel on a bed of clouds, dispensing digital blessings—or were they warnings?—to every floor…all seemed to be creepily insinuating their way toward her, crowding her, as if in deference to some rueful imperative of physics Danielle alone felt privileged, or maybe cursed, to perceive.

Did that make her very drunk, she wondered, or very sober? Either way she would not have minded lying down.

"Hey, you OK?" Theo's voice, as if to forestall any thoughts of litigation, was reedy with benign paternal concern. "You look a bit glazed around the gills."

"Just something I ate, probably."

"You didn't care for the restaurant, did you? I could tell. You had this vertical crease of disapproval on your forehead, like a pitchfork. What was the problem? The salmon wasn't line-caught enough? The arugula came in on a truck?"

"It was just a little, I don't know. Heavy."

"Substantial, you mean."

"Actually, I mean more like leaden."

"Ach, you Brooklyn people," he said. "It never ends. I'll have you know that place gets three stars in the Michelin Guide. Ranks top five on all the search engines. Check out the comment threads. Awesome. Amazing. An incredible experience. Something of a landmark even."

"They say Chernobyl's something of a landmark too," she said.

"Nice." Theo huffed a little breath onto his glasses, trying to rub the lenses clean with the end of his scarf. "What were you and Guillaume talking about by the way? You looked very chummy and conspiratorial over there in the corner."

"His daughter's applying to college. He wanted my take on the merits of Stanford vs. Princeton."

"What did you tell him?"

"I told him I went to SUNY Purchase."

"Wait," Theo said, "did I know that? Not that it matters."

"Why would it matter?"

"It doesn't matter," he repeated vaguely, in a way that suggested he was not even close to done thinking about whether or not it mattered. "Honestly, I'm surprised the guy *has* a daughter. He's so fidgety and unstable. Did you notice how every twenty minutes he gets up and goes out to smoke? What's up with that?"

"He's French?"

"He's Québécois. I don't think he even *does* smoke. It's just some power play. Probably he's out there checking the hockey scores. He owns a team you know. Also a distillery. Also a couple of lumber yards."

"I think there may be a racetrack somewhere too," Danielle said.

"Oh?"

"Mmm. He kept leaning over to show me pictures of his fillies. It gave me something to look at while he sort of accidentally felt up my knees under the table."

"Bastard," Theo muttered. "Is that a thing people do?"

"I'm not sure about people. It's a thing men do."

"Ah." At last the elevator arrived. The brass doors splayed open, neatly severing their reflections in two. "Interesting."

"Is it?" Yawning, she stepped to the back of the car, ready to call it a night. With the first abrupt, sluggish lurch, her face went hot, her knees turned spongy. She clutched her bag to her chest like you would a flotation device. As they sailed up over the atrium, she was more conscious than she wanted to be of the nutty Moroccan scent of Theo's hair oil, and the faint, tumid pressure of his breath against her cheek, and the various constituents of her evening meal mingling around sullenly, dolorously, in her stomach. The red wine, the fatty fish, the fried potatoes, the buttery beans, the oozing triple crème cheese, the tarte tatin, the plump and bulbous profiteroles…all seemed to be getting along badly, finding no points of interest in common, only their shared loathing for this cramped and sodden event space to which they'd been consigned.

"I have to say, that surprises me about Guillaume." Theo rotated his shoulders to loosen them, as though preparing for a game of squash. "He's supposed to be so happily married and all."

"So?"

"To that guy Paul across the table."

"So?"

"So nothing. It's just interesting, that's all."

Interesting being Theo's default phrase for observations he found both interesting and not interesting, it wasn't clear how to take this, and Danielle was too fatigued to try. Through drooping lids she watched the hotel scenery flash past: the clustered club chairs receding below, the slatted ceiling looming above, the terraced floors and artificial foliage slipping away noiselessly to the sides like so many boosters off a rocket. Were they rising, she wondered, or was everything else falling? At some point she looked up to find Theo examining her face with clinical interest, one foot wedged between the doors to keep them from closing. Around them the elevator dinged repeatedly, a moronic child banging a toy piano, unable to conjure a song.

"C'mon," he said, "let's get you into bed."

OK whatever, she thought. Let it go.

Together they navigated a passage down the sea-green corridor, past the blockish, stolid peninsula of the ice station, and up to the door of her room, where Theo bobbed around benignly in her peripheral vision, checking out the abstractions of the wall art, while she rummaged through her shoulder bag for the key card. Which appeared to be missing for some reason. Perhaps she had left it down at reception, she thought. Or perhaps it was still in the back seat of the cab, along with her antacids, her printout of the ten best local coffee bars, and her French phrase book with its list of blithe, inoffensive colloquialisms for leave-taking. *Au revoir, à bientôt, à plus tard, fuck off.* Anyway she couldn't find it. Her fingers fumbled blindly through the bag, rubbery and slow. She was aware of Theo Mirsky studying her in profile, ticking off her features in the same casually concentrated way he'd reviewed the wine and dessert lists earlier, like a man running cost-benefit ratios in his head. That was how you moved through the world as a data-driven decision-maker: weighing the variables, calculating options, making nuanced calculations every step of the way. How much of your capital were you willing to spend?

"Aha," Theo beamed when she produced the key card at last. "You see? The answer to our problems is always closer than we think."

Why was he talking to her as if she were a child? And why was she nodding so compliantly, as though listening like one?

Around them the radiators gurgled like fountains. Gasps of love—they might have been tiny, exquisite suffocations—leaked through the doors. She watched a room service cart jingle by and proceed down the corridor, trailing fragrant steam from its Kremlin'd domes. Nothing like a four hundred dollar a night room for which someone else was paying, Danielle thought, to generate the friction of licentious longing, the burgeoning imperatives of acquisitive materialism rubbing up against the fabric of anonymous dread. And was she herself immune? In the unlikely event she ever managed to gain entry to her own room, she knew more or less what she'd find: the chocolate truffles ornamenting the pillows, the little bottles of imported booze in the mini-fridge, the vials of expensive-looking hand lotion laid out on the vanity, all of which would inevitably in the course of time make their way into her purse. Did she need these things? Did she even want them? Would she wind up, on some level or other, having to pay for them? Not all these questions seemed to her entirely theoretical.

Meanwhile, Theo continued to hover attentively over her shoulder, watching her insert the card in the door-slot, eyeing her technique but withholding any analytical commentary or judgment.

Nothing happened. The handle froze; the light blinked red.

"Shall I try?" Theo ventured mildly.

"Try what?"

"The card. I think you've got it upside down."

"Really?" She felt a slow, drifting sensation of panic, as if she were being visited by one of her old childhood anxiety dreams, showing up late for a test she had neither studied for nor been notified of in a subject area she couldn't name. "I don't think so."

"Let me show you."

Danielle hesitated. As long as she was the one holding the card, whatever designs may or may not have been taking shape might still be arrested, she thought, or at least slowed down, or at least held off long enough to determine whether they accorded in even the most oblique way with her desires. As for Theo's desires, they were hard to read. He wavered beside her, breathing shallowly but noisily through his mouth, as if from some effort of exertion she couldn't see. The lenses of his glasses—as if in accord with some universal dictate that every effort to see better inevitably left you seeing worse—were smudged with the very fingerprints he'd used to clean them earlier. Behind them his eyes looked congenial but abstract. Was he patronizing her or hitting on her? Or was he only bored? Very much to his credit, or maybe a little against it, he seemed to have resigned himself to a course of stolid, watchful impassivity, neither pushing the situation forward nor absenting himself from it nor frankly doing much of anything else. Maybe it was some zen thing, who knows. He had an affinity for that stuff, for cut-and-pasted sutras and koans lifted from arcane eastern practices. *The truth*, he'd told her once, *was a shy deer in the forest*. You had to *make yourself a clearing* or it wouldn't emerge. There had been more along those lines, Danielle recalled, more knowing, ruminant-animal wisdom, though the conversation had foundered shortly after on the shores of her not-listening.

"Hold up," she said. "If that *wasn't* Guillaume futzing with my knees at dinner, who was it?"

"Ah." Theo winced a little, as if from some obscure but localized pain. "Interesting question."

"Is it?"

"Oh yes." He stared into her features like a man arrested before a window, tracking the flight of a bird. "A very interesting question. A question well worth thinking about, actually."

Danielle nodded. Behind her mind's dashboard a GPS was whirring, recalculating the routes that had brought them here even as it rifled through the database for alternatives ahead. She was not quite as drunk, it occurred to her, as she would have liked to be at the moment. Or was that the wrong way to let herself think? Her gaze ran down between the buttons of Theo's shirt, which afforded a partial glimpse of his torso: the pale, puffy mounds that rose around his nipples, the bones of his clavicles unfurling like wings above the tender heart-shaped indentations of his sternum. That a man was capable of growing breasts at his age seemed a poignant and encouraging development. Maybe time, for all the shit it got in the press, was like the global economy, another impersonal, irresistibly homogenizing force that sanded down the differences that kept people separate, washed away all arbitrary, protectionist borders, and promoted a robust free trade in empathies and resemblances that benefited everyone, lifting all boats. Was that too utopian a view?

Nonetheless it had to be said: right now, bottom line, the man only half attracted her sexually. And for all she knew the same was true for him. And then of course once you started multiplying fractions, you were rarely left with a whole number, only smaller and more troublesome fractions, thinner and more anemic slices of the pie. She thought about Karl, her nominal boyfriend, supine on their futon in Bushwick, scrolling through the latest sports highlights and political tweets on his various monitoring devices. She thought about Luke and Gabe, Theo's goofy, underachieving twins, whom out of some misplaced charitable impulse toward the children of unhappy marriages she'd personally made latkes for the previous Hanukkah, a gift of time and labor that had left vegetable grease splatter-painted over her backsplash and her knuckles bloody and raw and for which, it now occurred to her, she'd never been properly or even improperly thanked. She thought about Eileen, Theo's soon-to-be-ex-wife, a frank, funny, and formidable woman with a pair of magnificent swimmer's shoulders and the proximate smell and complexion, as well as the ass of a just-picked peach, a woman whom in a less fucked-up heteronormative environment Danielle might well have enjoyed sleeping with, in all honesty, more than her husband. Was Theo thinking about them too? Was he doing any brain work at all? You'd never know it from his expression, which remained placid, sleepily inert: a sea without waves, a desert without camels or tents.

Here was a man who knew how to make himself a clearing, all right. A clearing where nothing could possibly grow.

"I think maybe I'd rather not think about it tonight though," she said at last. "I mean if that's OK with you."

"Sure," Theo said. "That's fine. Perfectly understood."

"Nothing personal or anything. It's just I'm really beat right now. Among other things."

"Hey, it's fine, Danny. Really. No explanation necessary."

Fine, not fine; in truth Theo seemed equally content with either option. He was a big picture guy. You took a shot, you won or lost, you moved on. You didn't waste time round-tabling the nuances, rehashing your data, questioning your matrices and methodologies. Leave that to your employees. That was what you paid them for. Let them stay late at work, slouching over their laptops with their triple-shot espressos, their bike-delivered burritos; let them sit there ranking likelihoods of occurrence and severities of consequence on five-point spectrums while the sun flickered and flared and then ground itself out in that smoldering ashtray, the Meadowlands. Theo Mirsky for his part had other, more pressing things to do.

Or did he?

The thing was, Theo still hadn't moved away exactly. Not in any objective, spatial sense. If anything, he was now standing, in the objective, spatial sense, an inch or two closer than before. Or was *she* the one standing an inch or two closer? It was a question of perspective, she supposed.

Say a deer edged, on timorous legs, out of the surrounding forest, only no one around could quite get it together to see it. What happened then?

In all other senses of course nothing had changed. They were still standing out in the hallway. Her hand was still on the key card. The key card was still in the slot. The slot was still in the door. The rooms of the eleventh floor were still lined up like a jury, close-faced and silent, waiting for the trial to get going. And then as if by way of opening argument a phone buzzed in someone's pocket—they felt more than heard it—and both of them jumped.

"Yours or mine?" Theo asked, with no evident irony or air quotes whatsoever.

"What?"

"I said –"

"Oh for fuck's sake." In a sudden access of rage she pushed the door open behind them—which had been unlocked for some time apparently. The hissing *swoosh* it made, swinging inward over the carpet, was like the sound of a shredder laying waste to half a dozen guidelines Danielle herself had advocated for inclusion of in the HR handbook. "What difference does it make?"

The next morning, having awoken to the cry of a solitary bird, she could feel the difference inside her. She performed a quick inventory, trying to trace it to its source. Her mouth was parched, her head logy, her stomach desultory, her vagina smeary, ill-used. Otherwise she felt more or maybe less OK. She reached for her phone and pushed the Home button, like a patient calling for medication. No numbers or green-lit messages arrived. She had forgotten to plug it in.

She slipped quietly out of bed, a light, diminutive presence, easily erased. For a number of reasons, not all of them admirable, she was relieved that the other body in question, when she removed her weight from the mattress, didn't stir.

In the bathroom she took a moment to inspect the pouchy, evasive face in the mirror before subjecting it to a series of vengeful molestations. She scoured off her makeup with a scratchy cloth. She harassed her gums with waxen string. She attacked her teeth with abrasive paste. She dive-bombed her hair with a kamikaze brush, splitting the ends, tearing out the clumps. When she could find nothing else to gruelingly violate she stepped into the shower, where she scalded the living fuck out of herself before re-emerging to stand flushed and dripping on the carpet, her skin angry with scarlet patches like the devil's own flower garden.

Back in the room, she took a moment to review the other body in question in the milky half-light from the airshaft. True, when you're awake, every sleeping body looks alike, every woken one awake and unhappy in its own way. But there was something about the posture of *this* other body—its carelessly intrepid deployment against the sheets, the casually proprietary arrangement of its legs, the heedlessly outflung semaphoring of its arms—that told what seemed to Danielle, at this particular juncture in world history, an all too familiar story, yet another neoimperialist adventure narrative about a slow upriver slog, a dogged exploratory journey into the heart of her personal space, that dark, verdant valley between her thighs.

The residue of which excursion she still felt inside her by the way, even now: cool, viscous, stickily palpable, like sap from a toppled tree.

But fine, whatever. For the moment, she tried to put that aside. Tried to review the other body plainly and unsentimentally in the clear epistemological light of morning, as she would any other physical-commodity-based asset class it had fallen to her to evaluate. Certainly in this light the other body's infrastructure looked healthy enough. The other body's limbs looked solid enough. The other body's teeth looked straight enough. The other body's waterways, forking and blue-veined, were sufficiently throbbing with commerce to suggest a functioning, even robust market at work. The pale pink range of the other body's ribcage, the expansive mineral deposits of the other body's belly, the sleek deforested plains of the other body's shins (impressed with webby patterned grooves from the other body's socks)...all appeared to be the beneficiaries of a series of solid, well-intentioned maintenance policies drawn up and administered by some blandly progressive client-state—Canada, say—Danielle could admire from afar, without having any particular desire to revisit.

Pish-tosh, she thought, pulling on her leggings and sweater, what was the big deal? The other body on the bed, from whatever angle one reviewed it, lay well within her historical standard of deviation. She had slept with worse. So why was she crying then? Wasn't the world full of people who slept with people they had no particular desire to sleep with? Wasn't that what kept the economy going?

These and other questions occupied her for the length of time it took to go over to the pod machine, make a cup of thin, acrid coffee, and drink it down like medicine. Then she drew the crushed pod from its chamber, looked at it for a moment—wrung out, disposable—and set it primly on the vanity, reluctant for some reason to throw it away.

Meanwhile, the optics on the bed remained more or less what they were. The man upon whom her employment depended lay inscribed across the sheets, messy and aslant, like a hastily drawn signature on a contract. She watched his chest inflate and subside. His penis slumped shyly against one thigh, as if unable, or unwilling, to hold up its head any longer. True, the previous night's performance had not exactly been a tour de force of Tantric subtlety. But never mind, she thought. It didn't matter. This sucker was closing out of town. Time to drop the curtain, fold up the stage flats. Just one more undermotivated, sloppily executed drama to put behind her, Danielle thought, zipping up her carry-on and lifting it over the doorsill.

Out in the corridor people were rustling around crisply in expensive clothes, dragging wheeled, compacted luggage behind them. Danielle smelled all the usual morning fragrances: shampoo, aftershave, body wash, freshly applied lotions and powders. The only off-note was her; in her haste to get out of there she'd somehow forgotten to apply deodorant. So be it, she thought. Better to go forward than back. Better to hold up her head, bear the traces of her travels, come what may, even if they repelled and repulsed her.

The elevator loitered a few yards away, open-mouthed and indolent like an accomplice.

Je ne regrette rien, she told herself, and slapped the Down button with the flat of her hand. Just hard enough to hurt.

CARRIE COOPERIDER
Fawn

No, no, no—that's not how it goes. I'm putting too many words in. Start again. I should tell it so that it begins with silence, with snow, show you the frozen speckle-strewn fawn I found at wood's edge behind the cabin's bark-stripped walls. I should tell it so that a six-year-old can understand because that's what I was and that's all I knew.

I drew my breath in when I saw it, and felt the hairs in my nose stiffen to needles. Snow caked the cable stitch of my mittens and my fingers made fists inside. My toes were icebergs floating somewhere off the coast of my feet, unfelt, and my thighs were stinging hot with cold. I released my breath into fog. The fawn stood on unbending legs, muffled in its last snowfall; no answering steam came from its muzzle. Tiny icicles dangled from its snout and belly and I walked closer to touch my bare fingers to the frozen eyelashes that sparkled around an unblinking eye. Its head was bent to the left distance—looking where? Listening for what? The little deer had just stopped, it seemed, mid-step, mid-thought, the odor of snow still in its nostrils. The sudden spring storm had made the fawn too cold to walk any farther, its blood growing slushy and slow until its will to move left it. How long did the fawn's mother wait for her child to overcome his stubborn foolishness before bounding away into the grove of fir, turning her head one last time to look back, then vanishing into the dim wood?

The fingers of my uncovered hand grew stiff. I could not find my mitten. I must have dropped it when I pulled it off to touch the deer's spiky eyelashes, and it now lay hidden in the same-colored snow. Mother would be cross about the lost mitten, but it was already near-dark.

Leave it, then, leave it and go home, to warmth and supper and Mother. Mother, who would be starting to miss me—wouldn't she? Mother, who might be angry enough to send me straight to bed but too tired to take up the switch beside the door. Mother, who, I imagined, would just now be turning her head from some task to peer through the window's false brightness, seeking, among the deep blue shadows, her dear heart, her own dear darling—oh, wouldn't she be?

ASHLEE CREWS
Day One

It was barely daylight when she left him on the porch. Hearing her stir, he'd gotten up, followed her around the house, his hair a mess, his eyes sunken, sleep-deprived. "Mama," he said to her, a thing she relished, because up until Charles went to prison, he never called her this. "What's that?" she said.

"When you going be back?"

"Way before dark, darling," she said. "Way before dark."

"You think we might go fishing, like you said? Over at Dr. Duke's place? *Please.*"

She looked at him—Bryce, her brother's child, her nephew, twelve years old. She wanted what he wanted, which was just to have a little fun. Some peace and joy. It was summertime after all. "Just might can," she told him. "Run on in the house now. Get cool. It's hot out here."

He was afraid of ghosts, and she worried he'd sit out on the porch until she came back, would sit there in the swing glider with his eyes fixed on the gravel path that led all the way down to the highway, would sit there and wait on her, watch for her, not relax until he laid eyes on her again, not until she moved around the house again, enlivening it, stabilizing it. She worried he'd just sit there, outside, not even go inside to pee, not even go inside to watch television, just sit there, scared and waiting. All too well, she understood him. What she did not want—could not allow—was for him to understand this about her, how well she understood him.

Now, as she watched him ease up and reluctantly go inside to stand there at the screen door as if going too deep within the house might put him at risk, her left eyelid twitched, and her hands shook, and the queasiness that would not release her caused her mouth to water. She'd begun to pray, finding comfort in Mark 1:35: "Very early in the morning, while it was still dark, Jesus got up, left the house, and went off to a solitary place, where he prayed."

Staring at her nephew staring back, one final time, him shaded behind the screen, she turned her car around in the yard and pointed its headlights down the gravel path, thinking how true it is, what she'd told him, "It's the living that can hurt you, son, not the dead."

Until now, all her life, she'd said she believed in God. By not thinking about Him much at all. How crazy, she thought now, to have grown up in one church too—Mount Hebron Baptist—to have been baptized at twelve in the creek running beside it, to have worn a gold cross around her neck shortly afterward and forever more, to have gotten married at its altar, to have buried her parents and a brother in its side field, to have gotten the Christian fish decal and displayed it on her rearview window, but to have never read the Bible at all.

Certainly, she'd never needed it like bread and wine. In fact, she had felt nothing but disgust for those who did, though, until now, she would not have labeled the feeling disgust, but disgust it was, a cringing in her deepest being, the sight of their great neediness causing her to want to bolt out of the church, to go home and watch something good on television. It made her hungry, for potato chips, for comfort food, for anything but *that*, whatever that was, that weakness, that level of hunger and thirst.

Now, out on 15, the house a mile behind her, she watched the sun filtering through the pines, its gentle light that would be ablaze in no time, the highway pavement becoming hot enough to fry an egg.

Now, she'd become a woman who ate breakfast with God.

Now, when she saw the sun, she no longer saw the sun, but rather God, her Maker, *her* Creator. Months ago, she started in Genesis. And now she could feed herself a line or two. "First this: God created the Heavens and the Earth—all you see, all you don't see. Earth was a soup of nothingness, a bottomless emptiness, an inky blackness. God's Spirit brooded like a bird above the watery abyss. God spoke: 'Light!' And light appeared. God saw that light was good and separated light from dark. God named the light Day, he named the dark Night. It was evening, it was morning—Day One."

Glancing over at the passenger seat, sitting there, like a companion, Mavis looked at it, a straw basket of homemade strawberry muffins beneath a red gingham dishcloth, a basket of muffins made for him, for Charles.

"Day One," Mavis said now, driving forward toward Charles, her husband of forty years, a man that a woman at church had said, while grinning from ear to ear, "would soon be frying in hell."

The trip to hell would take an hour and a half, that was how long, one hour and a half Mavis had to get herself right, and to set herself straight, but even five long deep breaths, she discovered, couldn't touch this. "Wouldn't do it I was you," Dr. Duke told her, last Monday, at their weekly session.

"I thought you didn't give advice," Mavis replied.

"Well. You're the exception!" Dr. Duke said, leaning forward, with her eyes ballooned out. "And here it is. Here's your advice: Take that precious boy of yours fishing. Don't put that child through one more thing else."

Dr. Duke's office, for one short season, had been next door to a coffee shop—but Dr. Duke's office didn't last beyond that one winter. Next thing Mavis knew the woman had packed up and reopened way out on Johnson Dairy Road, which just seemed crazy, so far back, so far out.

Crazy until Mavis met the woman. "Nobody in this damn town," Dr. Duke confessed to Mavis, their first session, "was going to park on no damn courthouse square and walk through no damn shrink's door. I must have lost my ever-loving mind," she said, laughing, while resting her eyes on a cow pasture out the window, on two young Holstein calves standing at the fence. "Look," Dr. Duke said, turning serious. "How about Bryce come see me?" she said. "How about make him an appointment for next week? I'd like to get him talking too."

Dr. Duke—formerly known as Erica Finley. Half Mavis' age. Thirty years old. Oh, child, Mavis thought, when first sitting down on the woman's couch, how in God's name can *you* help *me*? But the woman had, immensely, the woman having some combination of small-town sense and Duke-educated book smarts. Born and raised in Mount Hebron, she'd made the local papers a decade earlier, the valedictorian from Mount Hebron High on her way to Duke University. Not one person in town could name another person who'd ever done such a thing. Not one person. Not to Duke University! Now, Erica's name could not be said without adding the word *Duke*, as if it were stamped on her like an official royal surname.

"Could've set up shop anywhere," Mavis said to the woman, their first session, the window screen raised behind Dr. Duke's chair, the smell of cows blending in with a lemongrass-scented candle. "Why come back here?"

Right away, that first session, Mavis went about asking all the questions. And Dr. Duke let her. Thoughtfully, Dr. Duke answered. "I've asked myself that more than a time or two," she said, pausing. Then, sighing heavily, as if place were a gruesome burden, she said, "Listen. I got this one friend. Lives out West. It's like a damn playground out there. She's all the time on Facebook in front of a waterfall. Or some majestic something or other with a rainbow piercing through. Know what I'm saying? She grew up in West Virginia. Near a mountain with its head blown off. And it's like you could read that on her. Until the West claimed her. Now she's got skin so smooth you'd think she was an unspoiled beauty. Fishing, I reckon that's why. I had to look hard for the beauty here. It's here. But not like a waterfall. I wanted to come home. Be close to Mama and Daddy. Have us all fish. I swore I'd never move back to the 'compound.' That's what I call it. Mama and Daddy, Aunt Ruthie and Uncle Bill, Granny June, and Papa Jim—all of their houses, you know, right there on that one piece of land. A big catfish pond in the middle. Them shouting across it. 'Hey, Ruthie! You got a cup of sugar? How about some flour?' Listen. I had job offers all over.

"Coming out of Duke. One right in the heart of San Francisco. But then I had Aida. And Aunt Ruthie had a stroke. And Mama and Daddy are getting on up in age. And I just decided to come on home. I wanted Aida and me to fish. Every weekend in the summer. Go swim. She just turned two. The apple of me and her daddy's eye. And then, you know—her daddy, my husband—we met at Duke. When he got done with Divinity School, Mount Hebron Baptist was looking for a preacher, and I joked with him about it; I said, 'Oh Lord, Ryan, they bad off if they hire you.' But they sure did. They hired him. Now. Let's talk about Bryce. The apple of *your* eye. He just turned twelve, right? You said him and his daddy went fishing. And when his daddy died, and he came to live with you and Charles, it was all he could talk about. Fishing with his daddy. And then Charles started taking him, right? Though Charles never actually took him fishing. He just lied about it."

Oh, those first sessions, Mavis remembered now while driving, how very much she had not wanted to talk about Bryce, or any of it, how she just wanted to listen, to be quiet with another human being, a safe human being, to sit still and just listen, to not be left alone, to not feel like a sitting duck or an orphaned girl. Looking down at the carpet, not answering the question, Mavis had said, "People. They come out here more?"

"Yep, they do," Dr. Duke said, accepting that Mavis needed more time, more space, to open up, to truly tell the truth. "Business booming now," Dr. Duke said, laughing easily, "Now that I've parked my station out in the boondocks." Turning serious again, she added, gently, "Maybe not today, Mavis, but at some point, I'm going to need you to..."

"Bryce," Mavis said, suddenly, blowing all the air out of her lungs. "God!" she said, shaking her head. "You ever get scared out here?" she asked, with her head still bowed to the carpet. "You know, being a woman out here alone in the woods with nothing but the crazy?"

"You were scared, weren't you?" Dr. Duke said. "A long time. Isn't that right?"

"Oh yes," Mavis said, reaching over to pick up one of Dr. Duke's big, soft couch pillows, to clutch it, without realizing it, like a hurt child. "Yes. A long time."

Now, Mavis' car ran off the road a bit, crossing over the white line, making the whole car rumble and vibrate. So lost in her head, she was. All the time. The fog and confusion of her mind. "Jesus!" she said, frightened. I can't afford to die now, she thought, suddenly grasping thin air for a Bible verse, as if it were a tree limb to reach up and hold, like some tangible salvation against the strength of a flood. That's how bad it had become. Bible verses—she posted them everywhere.

And yet, though they were everywhere, in plain sight, it was like a secret, a secret she felt almost ashamed of, as if the sight of them, all these strips of paper taped to the bathroom mirror, the refrigerator, the bed post—even across the horn on her steering wheel—showed nothing more than how close to the edge she'd come to reside. "Lean on, trust in, and be confident in the Lord with all your heart and mind and do not rely on your own insight or understanding. In all your ways know, recognize, and acknowledge Him, and He will direct and make straight and plain your paths—Proverbs 3: 5, 6." This verse, she'd slapped on her steering wheel, earlier in the morning, before daybreak.

Turning the steering wheel now to veer right, she realized she was almost there. To Hell. Down one more road, one more path, and there Google maps said it'd be: the Georgia State Prison, just outside Reidsville, Maximum Security, with only the most dangerous in the state housed there. Used to, back when they had death row, rumor was they'd invite volunteers to fry a man for twenty-five bucks. Mavis didn't know if this was true or not. What she did know to be true was this: Dr. Martin Luther King, Jr. had been sent here, middle of the night. Folks thought sure as this world he'd get lynched. But he didn't. He got released. Something Mavis wanted to rub in Charles' face, but by the grace of God would not. Instead, she'd keep her mouth shut and pray, for herself, for Bryce, for peace, for the victim's loved ones, and even for her husband, she guessed, because Charles—her husband, of forty-plus years—would never again see light over any other land.

"Life," this is what the judge said.

Charles, he blamed her. Entirely. And Mavis, though she tried to hide it from Dr. Duke, could not hide the guilt, her own guilt, for "betraying" him, for being "disloyal," for "murdering" him, as he liked to say, pointing his finger at her, the last time she saw him.

"You think I'm psycho?" Mavis asked Dr. Duke, in their most recent session, "You know, to want to look him one last time in the eye? To tell him I love him. That Jesus loves him. That I forgive him."

"I'm concerned you want to tell him that you're sorry," Dr. Duke said. "And I wish you'd stay home and let us work on that."

"No," Mavis said, indignant. "Of course not! Why would I want to do that?"

"You tell me," Dr. Duke said.

Now, Mavis looked at the speedometer. Slowing down, she tried to remember what she had told Dr. Duke in the end. Mixed up, she'd cried, at last. I feel so mixed up. Maybe I want *him* to say *he's* sorry! "Yes," Dr. Duke said, "and we can work through that, but seeing him I don't believe is the path forward, do you? Won't it just retraumatize you, and haven't you had enough of that? Why don't you not go," Dr. Duke suggested, "and take the boy fishing instead?"

*

Now, Mavis thought of Bryce, and thinking of him, her heart somersaulted. Was he back out on the porch? Was he still standing at the screen? He no longer slept. She no longer slept. Not sleeping, they now shared his bed, side by side, managing only breathing, jagged breathing, him whimpering after dozing off, then shooting up as if he'd forgotten, momentarily, that lying back was a dangerous thing to do. With hot tears running down his cheeks, his eyes widened, he'd become insistent, panicked, saying, "Mama! It was *not* an accident," with her saying, holding him tight, "I know; I believe you; I know."

"He *meant to*," Bryce would say, bending forward, clutching his stomach, his forehead against the mattress.

Still driving forward, she could hear him, in her mind, him calling her "Mama," the way he said it. His biological mother, her last known whereabouts Macon, not a birthday card sent, no Christmas acknowledged. In Mavis' mind, she could hear herself call him "son," the way she said it, calling him "son." Her and Charles, one miscarriage after another. Up ahead now, she spotted a church, an empty gravel parking lot where she could turn the car around, where she could rush back home, in the opposite direction of Charles.

But, within seconds, the opportunity passed, and her mind was set again on Charles, imagining him locked in a cell for the rest of his life.

"I'm convinced," Mavis had told the police, showing up at the station, "that my nephew is not lying. I believe Charles did it. Yes," she'd said to the police, "It's a shack, on Charles' daddy's place, can't miss it. About the only thing standing is the chimney. Well, you know, you've driven by it a hundred times. It's up on the hill. Nothing but it and that big oak."

Driving on now, she felt driven, possessed, pushed forward by something confounded. Whatever it was, it felt deadly, as though it could actually kill her. How fast can the heart pound, and for how long, before it wears out, she wondered, her heart never calm, never settled? "*Please*," she said to Jesus, driving forward. "Please, please, please help me to receive *your* peace."

Turn around, turn around, turn around, a voice inside her said, but she did not. She did not turn around.

*

Now, three miles away from the prison campus, Mavis wracked her brain for one instance, one memory of remorse. Had Charles *ever* apologized for anything?

No, he hadn't. Never. Not that Mavis could remember.

Not even when things were obviously his fault. He was right. Always, in his mind, he was right. And if Mavis ever dared to press him for some inkling of a guilty conscience, he would raise his voice, and turn the tables on her so that she was the one sitting in the hot seat. In the end, it was Mavis who would apologize, no, not apologize, but rather grovel, saying, "Charles, I'm so sorry, Charles. Please speak to me. Please. I didn't mean to upset you. Won't you least look at me, Charles?"

The papers—the local papers, the national papers—CNN and FOX and MSNBC—all of them speculated about him, his mind, this kind of "White Man," this white man that she knew simply as Charles, a man she married shortly before her twentieth birthday. Did he feel bullied by liberals and feminists and college-educated elitists? Did he feel like he had to find a scapegoat because he felt like his needs had gone so unmet? Did he feel like his small town—Mount Hebron—was in decline, that there were no jobs, no hope or promise? Isn't it vital that we try to get inside this white man's mind? What did the wife know? Had she seen warning signs? Red flags? Was she just as responsible? What was his childhood like? Why aren't we talking about the victims? We must call this terrorism. Black lives matter. *Why* did Trump get elected? We must understand his supporters, their "plight," their "ordeal."

Mavis had never thought of any of this before, knowing only that Charles was mean. That he, as his mama told her on their wedding day, "has his daddy's mean streak, though I reckon you haven't seen it yet, have you, honey?" When Mavis thought of the woman, long dead now, all she could picture was the woman's head, the way it wobbled like the very elderly, though she'd only been forty. "Because he's mean," Mavis said, simply. "He did it because he's mean. Like his daddy was. Both of 'em. Mean."

Entering the prison campus, Mavis felt shocked by the building— white and huge, an enormous slab of concrete block rising up out of the middle of nowhere, with a watchtower at the top, a spire above. The American flag, up there, high on a pole, the Georgia state flag too, the harsh sunlight glinting against the metal, blinding her until parts of her vision were blotted out. Below, on the ground, a high fence surrounding this slab of a building, the sharp fence wound with coils of hotwire.

"Yes," Dr. Duke said, early on, "Talk about all the good memories you want."

"What about the good memories! What about the Good Charles?" Mavis had asked Dr. Duke, nearly screaming the question, as the sessions went deeper, further.

"*Who* was *that* man?" Mavis asked, while holding a long list of all the things Charles had done or said that were indications of a conscience, things that did not sway Dr. Duke, not even one microscopic bit. "A deacon," Mavis said, exasperated. "He was a deacon! Did I tell you that?"

"Yes," Dr. Duke answered, compassionately. "Several times."

"He sent money," Mavis said. "To Africa!"

Now, there was nowhere else to go. The car had arrived. Staying inside it, with her foot still on the brake, Mavis suddenly realized that she'd left the air cranked up on high, number four, the whole ride, and now she was shivering. How long had she been shivering? At sixty-two years old, she'd become a woman never seen without a wool cardigan. On the other side of the glass, out there, it was eighty-two and rising. She needed to get out. Get it over with. Say goodbye. Look him in the eyes.

See. One more time. One more last time. His eyes. His soul?

He'd driven Bryce out there, to his daddy's place, after he beat the girl right in front of the boy, forced the boy to participate in ways that the boy still would not say. Made him dig the child's grave. This much was known.

Tamisha Rogers, the victim, eleven years old, born right here in Mount Hebron, not but eleven years old.

"An animal," the sheriff said, later, off record, his face raw, his eyes shot through with red streaks. "Worse than an animal. All I could think about," he said, wiping his forehead with a handkerchief, "was when I saw that baby girl I saw my own baby girls."

"Self-pity and rage, these are his two real emotions," Dr. Duke told Mavis. "Cognitive dissonance," she said, holding Mavis' list entitled "Examples of The Good Charles" in her hand. "It's important you know what it is," Dr. Duke continued, "and that way, when it happens, you won't be alarmed. And you certainly won't feel ashamed. Just let it happen. You're going to remember the good times, the times you thought were real and good and true, and it's going to confuse you because, the very next minute, you're going to swing in the other direction, and you're going to imagine what he did to that poor girl and to your poor nephew, and you're going to hate yourself for longing for him, and you're going to blame yourself because he trained you to, and you're going to feel responsible because he trained you to, and this is how your brain will swing, back and forth, all night, all day, for a long time, but please, Mavis, please know, I believe we can integrate this, and one day, I believe, with a lot of work and patience and self-compassion, you're going to accept the whole of it, the reality of it, the truth of it. The worst thing you can do is condemn yourself. Watch your brain do what it's bound to do. And remember, you're having a normal reaction to a very abnormal situation."

Now, releasing her foot off the brake, Mavis unpeeled her hands from the steering wheel, then placed them on her lap as if in prayer. Sitting in the parking space, out front of the prison, she tried to watch her brain. Like it was some troubled entity outside her best self. Lifting her left hand, she locked the doors. She didn't know why. There were no killers running loose, and she was supposed to be getting out, going toward the one she married. "God," she said.

Feeling safe, with the car doors now locked, her eyes glazed over, and no longer was she in the car. There was no steering wheel. No dashboard. No green pickup parked to the left, no blue minivan to the right. The robin hopping in the sunburned grass in front of her hood, it did not exist.

No. Now, she was in Milledgeville, Georgia, with him, her husband of forty-plus years, and there they sat, on barstools at a high table inside Applebee's, the waitress so pretty and sweet they had to comment on it each time she came by, first bringing them cheeseburger egg rolls for appetizers, then recommending the cedar salmon for Mavis and the top sirloin for Charles, and tough call between the Bahama Mama Mucho and the Citrus Summer Squeeze. Her birthday.

Two bright drinks later and Mavis had felt nothing but warm. "I wish Mount Hebron," she told Charles, "would get an Applebee's." Looking out the window, she saw the Carmike 6. "And a movie theater," she said, remembering the old Pastime, still on the courthouse square, a theater they'd once gone to regularly, a place now empty, rust-stained, dark, and decaying.

"We ought to do this," she said youthfully. "All the time!"

Originally, they'd just ridden over for supper. Something they rarely ever did. To add a movie on was just pure unheard of. "I don't even know what's good," Mavis said, a half hour later, when Charles slid into a parking space, right in front of the Carmike 6, it busy and buzzing with life. "Oh, gosh," she said to him that night, as he walked chivalrously around the hood of the pickup and to her door to open it, to help her get her feet firmly on the ground. "Charles," she said, "Lord, shouldn't we do this more? All the time!"

This is how she would remember the first part of the night, as if the feeling had been a miracle in and of itself, her and Charles never giving themselves over so freely. After all, she'd offered to just cook supper for them. Maybe fry some shrimp. Sit out on the porch. Not make too big a fuss. But now, walking arm in arm with her husband, toward the theater, for a moment, it made her dream. Big dreams. Crazy dreams, like the Bahamas! Why couldn't they go? Charles and Mavis! Off to some fancy resort with lots and lots of pink drinks! Oh, she was about to say it aloud, but then, like the sobering effect of a sudden attack, Charles spoke.

"Hold up," he said, coldly.

"What? What is it? Charles, what is it?" It was then that she noticed his face: the disgust, the irritation. His face registering the exact opposite expression of tranquility. "Charles?" she asked again, this time more frantically—the inexplicable shame inside her filling her with dread, as if her face had only seconds to adapt, to compute, and to catch up. To balance things and make them right, no matter what the cause, which was still unknown.

"Go stand up there," he instructed. "Pick us out something," he said, roughly.

A ways off, up there, on a platform, a whole line of people waited to buy tickets. She had no idea what movie to pick, and she didn't want to pick wrong. She wanted him to help her. "I'll just wait," she said, cautiously, unsure of what it was she was waiting for.

"No! Go!"

"OK, OK, OK," she said, scurrying away from him, feeling as though her tail was tucked between her legs, the unbearable shameful feeling with her now, wholly, as if she'd done something wrong, but what something wrong she had no idea.

Now, Mavis returned to the prison, as if her brain had just decided that it was time for a break. Suddenly, she saw the robin hopping in front of her hood. What all, she asked herself, do we see and not see?

Looking over at the prison, she realized she'd been holding her breath, that her chest felt tight. Taking a gulp of air, she wondered if a guard was going to come out, ask questions: "Ma'am, why you taking so long to get out," she imagined him asking, knocking on her window with a billy club, or maybe, him saying, "Ma'am, you should just go home," or worse, "Maybe I should escort your guilty ass right in here with him. Maybe you ought to just sit your life out too?"

That night, that Milledgeville night, she picked Kong Skull Island. But knew nothing about it. Other than what she read: "When a scientific expedition to an uncharted island awakens titanic forces of nature, a mission of discovery becomes an explosive war between monster and man."

That night, that Milledgeville night, while her husband crawled back into his pickup, for no reason she could decipher, she stood inside the theater, buying them a large bucket of popcorn, extra butter, while watching him through a wall of tall windows, while trying to figure him out.

Not much later, sitting next to him in the freezing theater, with her hand deep in the warm bucket, she realized he'd been stuffing a gun in the back of his jeans, had leaned over and pressed his chest against the steering wheel in order to do so, that he'd returned to the pickup to open the glove compartment box, to get the pistol out, that his face had changed because he'd seen a group of people in the parking lot.

Teenagers. Black teenagers. That night, the whole audience—almost entirely teenagers. Black teenagers.

"Bunch of sorry-ass niggers," he said, right into Mavis' ear, just as the movie started. "They don't shut up," he warned her, easing his body forward, to unearth the pistol, "They going to wish they had," adding, "They don't learn to pull their pants up, they deserve to get shot in the fucking ass."

Next, he laid it—the pistol—like a rattlesnake right there across his knee, the cold dark barrel of it now pointing directly at the back of the next seat up, a seat with a child's spine and heart and lungs backed into its cushion.

*

Slipping back under, into the heart of that night, Mavis remembered confessing to Dr. Duke that she'd said nothing. "I couldn't hear. My hearing," Mavis said, "It went out."

And it had, straight out, like a tsunami, pulling her with enormous strength into absolute deafness only to rush back in the most acutely painful way: the thunder roll sound of the movie being played next door, the slurping sound of the Coke getting swallowed by the teenager on the other side of her arm on the armrest, the pulsing of blood shooting through her heart and into her ear canal.

"I got up. 'Excuse me,' I said," she'd told Dr. Duke. "Then I bumped into knee after knee after knee—all the way down the aisle—another knee, one more knee. 'Excuse me. Excuse me. Excuse me!' I stood in the aisle. To wait for him. To put pressure on him. Slow. He was so slow getting up. He seemed so in control. In those long seconds, all I could imagine was him cocking the gun at the whole theater and being *that* man, the man in the news. And yet I couldn't imagine it either. Not Charles. Not *my husband*."

"He didn't speak to me," Mavis said, locked inside her car, talking to herself, as though Dr. Duke were right there, listening in the passenger seat to her tell it all again. "I was so afraid. I can't tell you how afraid I was. We had to drive all the way back, you know, from Milledgeville to Mount Hebron, and it's nothing but country road," Mavis said. "Dark roads with nothing but nothing. A bunch of deer. He wouldn't even turn on the radio. I almost tried. But I didn't. I just kept my mouth shut and my hands in my lap. I thought he might kill me. Which just seemed crazy to me. Paranoid. He hadn't ever murdered anybody, not that I knew of! I mean, he had threatened to kill me a time or two. But see, and I know this don't make any sense, or maybe it does, but listen, I grew up with this stuff. Driving down the road, if Daddy saw a black man, he'd say, 'Ten points!' like it was nothing. Like he was being funny. I'm sure I laughed. I know it didn't bother me the way it should have. I mean, it was my daddy. And I knew he wasn't going to really hit the man. But listen. It mattered. Because then I ended up marrying a man. Know what I'm saying? Who could pull a gun! Like that! And for what? Teenagers? Teenagers acting like teenagers? God, I don't know. Daddy struck Mama. Lots of times. She never said it was wrong. She just told me to stay out of his way. When he got like that. And that's what I did with Charles. I just stayed out of his way. I expected him to be mad at me. And I know he was that night. But I expected him to *say* it. To make me pay. But he just stayed quiet. Of course, I did too. But it wasn't like him to stay quiet. And I guess that scared me the most. Anyway, we all made it home alive. And when I say that, I mean the teenagers too. But Charles saying nothing? Not yelling at me the whole way back? Not driving all crazy to scare me? Well. That. That worried me the most. That. That didn't sit right. I needed to talk to him about it. I wanted answers. But I knew better. Charles wasn't ever into conversation like that. And I was afraid. Really truly honest to God afraid of him that night. I couldn't even lie down next to him. I wanted to sleep anywhere else. I wanted to get Bryce and run. I stayed up. God, I don't know. Four in the morning? Just sitting in the living room. Watching National Geographic and televangelists. I finally made it to bed. Slipped in. Rolled over on my side, with my back against him. He was on his back, with his eyes shut. I remember that. The whole house was still. Quiet. Then. He spoke."

Oh, Mavis could not forget it, the sound of his voice, fissuring the night: "Next time you mind your own damn business, or it might be your ass gets shot."

"It wasn't even ten minutes later," Mavis said now, inside the empty car, "Before he was snoring. Snoring!"

Not long after that Milledgeville night, one evening, Charles, he'd dragged a kitchen chair into the boy's bedroom, and he was sitting next to Bryce, both of them staring at the computer screen. "What you boys up to?" Mavis asked, casually stepping inside the room to gather up a load of laundry, a sock on the floor here, a pair of pants over there.

"What you boys up to?" Charles asked her back, mocking her, his voice mean and high-pitched.

"I just came to get the socks," Mavis answered him, apologetically, while bending down next to the desk to get a pair of boxers. "Be out of your hair in no time," she said, hating herself, hating him. But loving the boy.

Rising up from the floor, she pushed her reading glasses down off the top of her head and pushed them against her nose. Adjusting the laundry basket onto her hip as if it were a small child, she leaned forward and squinted over the top of Charles' head.

"Fifteen minutes," she told them, "till supper."

Then, she walked out.

Only to return in the middle of the night.

Creeping down the hall, she entered Bryce's bedroom and bent over him to check his breathing, the way she would have a newborn. She unplugged his laptop, took it off his desk, and cradled it in her arms, then walked it back down the hall on feet like a cat and through the living room and outside to the porch, where there were no walls but the one wall—the house wall behind her rocking chair.

Out front, before her, there was just the tree line, and above that, an inky blue-black sky that went on eternally.

"Jesus," she said simply, before forcing herself to the screen, that now shone like a full moon, to read more, to digest more from this website.

What had she expected? Porn. Yes, that was it. She had expected porn. Not this.

"What," she whispered, "in God's name am I supposed to make of *this*?"

"And it's the gospel truth," she read, out on the porch that night, her eyes aching in the glare from the laptop screen, as she read one member comment after another, on the most racist notions in print she'd ever seen. "We Whites can't just sit by and…"

Deep in the night, after plugging Bryce's laptop back in, Mavis strategized ways to casually tell Charles that she'd take Bryce to school. That he didn't have to do it. That she'd do it. When the birds started singing, Mavis, having not slept, walked out to the chicken coop, as she often did, to gather an apron full of eggs. After coming back inside, the screen door falling shut gently behind her, she fried them all eggs and buttered the toast. As always, she smeared on grape jelly, but this time, instead of sitting at the table next to Charles, she took her own plate and went out to sit on the porch.

"Where're you going?" Charles asked her, noticing, as though long ago he'd handed her an invisible script and one small line out of order threatened it, his entire play.

"To get some fresh air," she responded, nervously, before adding, "I think this morning I'll drive Bryce to school."

But Charles, he cut her off at that. Cut, cut, cut, he seemed to say, his voice, full force, a tyrannical director's voice. "No," he said. "I do it," he said, sounding like an overgrown toddler, though he was no toddler; no, he was a man, a two-hundred-fifty-pound man.

So that morning, when Mavis watched him drive away with Bryce, who sat silently in the passenger seat next to him, the boy's face vacant, void of all boyhood, she determined to let the dust settle, then drive her car straight to the school, to pull the boy out, on account of an emergency.

To take him somewhere safe, to take them both somewhere safe, where she could do triage on him. On them. What, Bryce, she wanted to know, is plaguing you?

Now, she looked out her window at the prison. Could Charles, way up there, in a cell behind bars, look down and see her car? Witness her, hesitating? If he could see her now, would he mock her? Mock her for her pathetic insistence on making him good and right? On making him see *her* as good and right? Would he laugh at her total dependence on Jesus? The way she woke up now, unwell, unrested, and went out into the breaking light, each morning, with a cup of coffee, in order to pray to God for simple survival.

He'd taken such tender care of the chickens. This was one of the things on the Good Charles list. "Oh," Mavis told Dr. Duke, "you had to see it to believe it. The way he talked to them. The way he named them. He built them a mansion. A chicken mansion. Built them a perch to sleep on. Said it had to be at least two feet off the ground in order to keep the rats and mice out. The window trims he painted white and the front door red. They had them a little wooden staircase. Listen," Mavis told Dr. Duke, "I've been wringing chicken necks all my life. That might surprise you. But I grew up doing it. We had to eat! Charles, he wouldn't do it. He wouldn't even watch nobody do it either. Oh God, he told me, I could never do that! I'm too tender-hearted to do something like that!"

Now, Mavis counted the windows of the prison. And thought of Tamisha Rogers. Her tiny neck. And the fear in her eyes.

Just a girl, walking home from a cousin's house, minding her own business, when Charles bore down on her from behind, honking at her, hollering at her, out the window: "Don't make me get out and move you myself!"

"Oh," Mavis told Dr. Duke, "I believe he thought he was teaching Bryce a lesson. A lesson, in his mind, about respect. He expected the girl to cry. To run. And fast. To say how sorry she was. But she didn't. She shot him a bird. And kept right on walking, without looking back. Charles slammed on the brakes. And undid his belt."

Oh God, how he beat...

Now, Mavis pictured Charles' daddy's place, the shack on a hill beside an old oak she'd driven by a hundred times, the house long dead, hollow as an eye socket. The moon, it had been full that night, and Mr. Samuel Rogers, Tamisha's daddy, would come to say he'd been out using it to search for his baby girl, the same way he went on doing it, night after night, ever since his baby girl had gone missing, since she hadn't blasted through his door, on time that evening, with her sunshine disposition.

"Oh God, *why*?" Mavis had screamed alone in the car, one night, when she'd tucked Bryce into bed and ridden up to the crime scene, as far as she could get. There, with Charles having just gone to prison, she pictured Tamisha Rogers, this child of God, sought after by her father, in a shaft of moonlight, only to be swallowed up inside a white man's darkness, inside *her husband*—of forty-plus years—*his* dark side.

For another half hour, Mavis sat in the car, watching the robins, without seeing them at all.

Then, she spotted two children, two cars down, siblings, the brother and sister's mother having gotten Mavis' attention by shouting, after slamming the creaky car door shut, over her shoulder, as she walked toward the prison, "Stay! Don't get out!"

Expressionless, unmoving, the children never turned to their mother's voice but rather remained facing forward, their eyes set upon the robins. The interior of their car, Mavis knew, was already growing unbearably hot, though the children seemed to have done the math, calculating that the air outside was worse, far worse.

"*Jesus!*" Mavis said, angrily, forcing herself to not turn away, to see it, the deadness on these children's faces, a lifelessness no child's face should ever come to bear. Opening her car door, without thinking, Mavis stepped out, the basket in her hand, then walked behind their car, parked two cars down, her heart rate ticking, ever higher up, so high, so fast, that she stumbled, feeling faint, the short high waves crashing inside her chest, though this time, not from fear, but from rage, her own rage, a rage that seemed overpowering, so new it was to her system, as if her bloodstream had never known a thing but fear and shame. "I *will not* forgive you," she thought, staring up at the prison, its row of windows, before gently tapping on the car's backseat window, her voice, somehow, motherly, calm and measured. "Excuse me," she said, leaning down, to offer the muffins.

Oh how they jumped! Their shoulders, rising in unison, curling inward, as if to protect their very organs, the boy's hand cupping his mouth, the girl's eyes alert, alarmed, so alarmed, and then, so pissed. "What the shit?" the girl said, loud enough to be heard, and made known, through the glass.

Driving out of Reidsville—flying out of it at twenty miles over the speed limit—Mavis shook one arm out of her wool cardigan, then the other. Burning up, she thought of Tamisha Rogers, of her father, of Bryce, of the faces that would never return, would never, given no amount of time, come back.

"Trauma is a long road," Dr. Duke told Mavis last session. "But there's hope. Bryce," she said, "is not a Charles."

Now, all Mavis wanted, in all of this world, was to lay eyes on her son.

"Please, please, please," Mavis begged, barely slowing down to turn off 15. "How in the hell could I..."

Halfway up the driveway, rocks kicking up, dust swirling, she spotted him, his boy's frame, just twelve years old, him, on the porch, with sweat pouring off him, she could see now, flinging open her car door and leaving it open behind her, rushing up the porch steps to him, his arms crossed and locked around himself, his eyes, coming to life, for a moment, at the sight of her, as hers did, for a moment, at the sight of him, and then his, returning to vacant, staring out, now, again, beyond her.

"You 'bout ready?" she asked him, out of breath, the pain sharp in her chest. "To go…" she said, pausing, bending forward, to catch her breath, but instead of answering, he moved his eyes, back to hers, then stood up, and was gone, stepping back into the quiet house to get his fishing pole, his daddy's old cane pole, so they could go fish at Dr. Duke's pond, stepping back out with it now over his shoulder, offering her his mercy, so childlike, even still, in its miraculous hope, and undeserved tenderness.

"We better get," he told her, tiredly, when they got back on 15, she flooring it down the highway, it not even noon yet, the windows down, the hot summer breeze on their skin, she thinking, yes, yes, son, and catch us all the light we can.

Four Walls Around Me to Hold My Life

Sometimes I looked over at who I was married to forever. She was on her side of the bed, me on mine. It'll hit you now and then, this feeling.

I got up for work, and she said, "What's *your* problem?" But she didn't want to know.

I was throwing boxes for UPS. They hired me because of my physical size. I'd been working as a bouncer but got fired for not playing well with others. Now I was getting a paycheck and limited health coverage I'd need someday for my back.

My wife's name was Shelly, and she always seemed a little too pretty for what surrounded her. Including me. We were renting a duplex over in Gallatin, and it wasn't that bad—there was a Piggly Wiggly down the street—but I guess it wasn't all that good either.

One reason the rent was cheap was because a fire burned up the other half of the house before we got there. Now a tarp covered the roof and some charred framing. Put your face against the wall and you could still smell what happened on the other side to the guy and his cats. Most folks wouldn't put up with conditions like that. But I had all my life.

Something happened one night and got me thinking about things. Shelly was in what she calls her "study"—a word I'd never heard used for a room until I met her—and when I got home from work she was hiding in the hallway.

I asked her what was going on, and she said somebody was outside her window while she was studying in her study.

"You studying again?" I said.

"That isn't the point," she said. "I mean, I'm trying to get back into it, but this dude, like, came up to my window. While I was right here," she said, "in my own private house."

"Did he see you?"

"Why you think he stopped?" she said. "To clean the gutters? He had a gun, James."

"What were you wearing?"

She shook her head, looked away, and blew out a sentence that wasn't meant for me.

I'd warned her about walking around in her underwear. The blinds she'd put up weren't really blinds, just see-through, roll-down things made out of bamboo. Supposed to make the place feel like a vacation.

"Clothes," she said. "I was wearing clothes. OK?"

I did like how she looked in her panties, the ones with the eyelets in the fabric. I couldn't blame somebody for peeking. I'll admit, I'd once watched her from that same window. She hadn't heard my truck pull in and was doing normal evening stuff in her undies. And there was her husband, me, spying, trying to remember what it used to be like. I never told her about that.

"You aren't allowed to just come up on somebody's window," she said. "Specially with a gun."

"I wouldn't know," I said. "What'd he want?"

"He told me to…" She pretended to flash me. "He wanted to see them," she said.

"Did you?"

"I didn't want to get shot."

"Motherfucker." I ran to the window and came back. "What exactly did he say? Give me the words."

She summoned a stranger's voice, and said, "Show me your tits, bitch."

"Was he white or black?"

"I don't know. It happened so fast. And his face was covered."

"I like black people," I said. "I got a black friend at work. His name's Eddie."

"Here we go," she said.

I walked her into the bedroom and put her in bed and lay down next to her. I'd been working all day long and smelled of packing tape and cardboard and propane fumes from the forklift, but I still acted gentle and understanding—because I was. "Calm down," I said. "Everything's safe now."

"You got any smokes?"

"In my truck."

She found the keys in my pocket and got up. I asked her if she wanted me to go instead, but she said, "No, I'm good."

The fact she wasn't scared anymore got me feeling a little useless.

We shared a cigarette in bed without talking. Then she rolled over, and we must've both fell asleep because when I opened my eyes it was full dark in the room. I rolled onto my back and tried to keep an eye on the glowstar stuck to one of the ceiling fan's spinning blades. She put it there because she liked the swirling green circle it made above us.

Her hair smelled like shampoo and I put my fingers in it. After a while of getting spoony with her, I figured she was back to normal, so I kind of hunched in, hoping she was interested. She sniffled. Well, shit—now she was crying. And that's when I made the decision. "I'm gonna go get him," I said. "And when I do, I'm gonna put him in my sights and tell him to show me *his* titties."

She turned over and was looking worried. "That really isn't what I wanted to hear right now."

"Dude fucked with the wrong dude." I got out of bed.

"You don't still got your gun, do you?" she said. "After you promised?"

"I said I'd get rid of it when we had our kid."

She put her knuckles in her eyes.

"Sorry," I said. But it felt good bringing it up.

"This isn't about you," she said. "Or him. It's about me. What happened to me. Tonight. OK?"

"You aren't supposed to give these sickos what they want," I said. "They'll come back looking for more. They're like raccoons."

"You're making it sound like I did something wrong," she said. "He had. A gun."

"What was he wearing?" I said. "You remember what he looked like? Was he handsome?"

"Oh, my god," she said. "He had on a big coat. Something covering his face. A shirt or a mask or something. So yeah, I about creamed my pants."

"Ah," I said, shaking my finger like a clue, "but you weren't wearing any pants, were you? Give me an identifying feature. Just one."

"It doesn't matter what he looked like. He's gone now."

"Yeah, you said that already." I shook the walls stomping into the kitchen in my work boots and slung the fridge door open. She hadn't been shopping and I guess it's fair to say I hadn't been either. There was one old box of Chinese on the middle shelf that she'd been picking at. The meat was gone and all that was left were little corns in some brown sauce. A half-gallon of milk in the door. Three cans of Busch in the crisper labeled Lettuce.

We were just sipping beers every once in a while. We'd made an agreement to drink only if we were celebrating. Never if we were angry. But all I wanted right then was to hear the sound of one of those cold boys cracking open and take a mean gulp. I dropped the Chinese box in the shopping bag of trash hanging from the pantry doorknob. "I'm hungry," I said.

She said something back, but I was already into an idea. "James?" she said.

"I'm thinking right now," I said.

"Come back in here with me? I just need somebody near me right now."

"I'm taking a drive," I said. "I don't like what he did to you. I love you and you know that shit."

I walked out to my truck and noticed the passenger side door was unlocked. Then I saw the glove box was open. Napkins, receipts, a lighter, soy sauce packets, the warranty manual—all scattered across the seat and the floorboard. This wasn't her work. The cigarettes had been in the cup holder, where they always were. I came back into our bedroom carrying the junk from the glove box in my hands.

She was under the blanket. "What's that?" she said.

"Remember when you went out to my truck for cigarettes? What I always tell you to do?"

She thought for a minute, wasn't putting it together on her own, so I helped. "Lock," I said. "The fucking door."

I tossed the stuff on top of her and left it with her there to clean up. I drove to the liquor store and sat in the parking lot. People went in with nothing and came out with paper bags. Seemed like a good deal. Back in the cab, I sat with a bottle beside me. The first splash gave me the courage and direction to pull the jumper seat down and reach around until I felt the hard plastic safety case. Thank God. The crackhead, or whoever it was, was too lazy to look back in there. I opened the case with a key from my chain, and inside lay my little snub-nosed pocket buddy. Loaded and ready for debate.

I picked it up and smelled its oiled barrel, then returned it to the jumper hole along with the bottle. I didn't want to get drunk. Just chill. I went driving around our neighborhood, looking for somebody doing something. Anything. But it was just my headlights, everywhere I turned.

*

She was either sleeping or pretending to sleep when I got back in bed. All the trash was gone, like I'd never lost my temper, and I conked out right away. My eyes opened before my cell phone started going off. There she was on her side. Me on mine. That's what whiskey does to me. Wakes me up early and gets me looking deep into stuff.

I went into the kitchen, turned up the radio, and put on coffee. We kept tuned to my old man's AM station that played recycled country music. Every now and then he'd get on there and preach about local problems. Very offensive stuff, to Shelly. He wasn't popular with most folks our age, and I used to think he was crazy too, but lately I was starting to come around.

Across the driveway our neighbors were sitting out on their porch listening to their music. Some folks had to go to work. Some folks worked their butts off just for them to sit around and listen to that nonsense. But I'd actually never talked to them. And it was Saturday.

The neighborhood seemed peaceful when we first got here, but my dad was right when he told me, "You're an Alcorn, James. Trouble will find you. They don't like you. Just remember that."

He still lived back in Carthage, right on the Cumberland River where I grew up, and believed the water wouldn't let him leave. My brother, Dustin, went off to Iraq and my mom was still waiting to hear back from him. Shelly was with Dustin before me, before he left, and she was probably still waiting too. But I knew my brother better than they did, and though he wasn't dead to us, I was sure by then we were all dead to him. That's why I was cool about being with Shelly.

We got hitched when it turned out she was pregnant. We moved downriver to Gallatin so she could be close to Vol State Community College where she planned on studying to be a nurse. Or a vet tech. But she ended up losing the kid. I'm sure it was hard to be studying stuff like that in school and know every little word for what's going on inside.

She ended up taking time off. Believed the kid was my fault. Said I was naturally wilder than her and that was stressing her body out. And it's true, I was drinking a lot. I could tell she was thinking about how things might've been if she hadn't ever met her ex-boyfriend's big little brother. We were both hoping to improve our lives together, but one thing happened and then it all started slipping.

Today I was unloading cargo from a barge onto a truck. The river out past the loading docks was murkier than it was back in Carthage, and it smelled different too. A more junky industrial stink. You could see the greenish steam wafting off it in the heat. All I did was lift, turn, toss, repeat. It was a long shift, 7 to 7, but it only came around once a week. Tomorrow I'd be back on the forklift, zipping around inside the air-conditioned warehouse. It was a privilege to be in there driving that thing. You had to get an operator's license for it. Which I did. Shelly framed it and hung it up in our living room next to the picture of our wedding day. It meant a lot to both of us. Proof that I slowed down on drinking and found some purpose.

But the feeling I woke up with stayed with me all day. It was a shadowy man on the fringe of my vision. Either my brother or the guy who was watching Shelly last night. Maybe both. Now he was watching me. I couldn't shake him, couldn't even numb it with work. He just stood there waiting.

I was in the break room clocking out when Jeff stepped next to me and said, "What you up to? Wanna go somewhere?"

My time card read 19:13. Something about that number. I dropped it into its little slot and told him, "I quit drinking."

"I know this place," he said. "Cross the river?"

I pulled my phone out and called Shelly. "I'll be late," I said.

"But it's your favorite," she said. "For supper."

"Here's a hint," I said. "I don't got a favorite." And I hung up.

"There you go," Jeff said, slapping my back. "I can tell something's been wrong with you, man. Come on."

He gave me a lift to his house, where a bunch of boys were in the yard trying to catch a dog. It was a little neighborhood not too far from mine, and I could've left right then and went home for supper. Told Shelly I was sorry, didn't know what got into me. But instead I stepped into Jeff's place.

His bedroom looked like mine and that gave me the creeps. Only difference was they had nice heavy drapes over the windows.

"Where's your wife at?" I said.

"Good goddamn question." He took a bowl off their dresser, lit it up and handed it to me. "You ever feel like, you know, like, shit, I don't know."

"Sometimes," I said, blowing out.

He went through their top drawer and grabbed some cash. "Me and her's been saving it up," he said.

We stepped back out onto the front stoop, and the dog was stretched on the side of the road. All the boys were gone except one who was kneeling beside it. His shoulders were moving like he was laughing.

"Should've used bologna," Jeff called to him. "That's the only way she comes."

"Hush," I said. "That dog could be his."

"That wasn't his dog." Jeff lit a cigarette. "That dog was mine."

We took the bridge over the river. The wind up here was cool through the open windows. The barges down below looked like little Legos. We came back down and merged onto a cracked street with one row of low, collapsing brick buildings.

"Our little Aleppo," Jeff said, lighting a new cigarette off the last one. The old butt was smoldering between the knuckles of his steering hand.

"What's Aleppo?"

"It's like Iraq," he said.

"That's where my brother was stationed. Or still is."

"I don't know why y'all go join the army when you got shit like this right here. You want to shoot up some folks…" He flicked the butt out the window. "Just do it."

I didn't answer him, and after a while he asked what was wrong. "I didn't hurt somebody's feelings, did I?"

"I don't know shit," I said, and he thought that was hilarious. "My brother was in the army," I said. "Or the military or the navy or whatever." And we both lost it. "Damn," I said. "That weed's working."

We drove to a strip bar called Hindsight, shared a bottle of vodka in the lot and I got to thinking about what I'd been missing out on in life.

Inside, Jeff took a chair at the foot of the stage. But the girls were just too young, so I stayed at the bar. One of them came over and said, "That guy bought you a dance."

Jeff was waving his money at me while two girls grinded on him.

I followed mine into a room. She was wearing tiny panty things. Kind of like the ones I told Shelly not to walk around in. Before time was up, she asked what was wrong with me.

"Maybe I'm getting old," I said. "Can we just talk?"

She crossed her arms and pointed an ear at me, but I didn't know what to say. "How about this?" She slipped her panties off with a squiggle, spun around, and straddled my lap backward. She rocked around, and the shape of her hips on my lap looked like an upside-down heart. There was a birthmark down there.

"How about that," I said.

"Eh-eh-eh," she said. "No touching."

I got up and she fell to the carpet. "Shit," I said. "I didn't mean to." But it was too late.

"Go call your wife," she said, rubbing her ring finger at me. "Tell her where you are and how you don't got anybody to talk to."

The music cut off. I'd forgot it was there. "Your time's up," she said. "Plus, you broke my shoe." She pulled off one of her high heels and showed me the torn ankle-strap. "You better tip me enough to buy a new pair."

"Listen," I said. "My friend's paying for this. He's why I'm even in here." I pushed the booth's curtain open and stepped out.

The main room was busy. There was a lady floating in a cloud of purple vapor and laser beams. Men's hands held quivering dollar bills beneath her. Marilyn Manson was pumping through the speakers—*the beautiful people, the beautiful people*—and I didn't see Jeff anywhere.

I took my phone out to call him, but a bouncer grabbed my arm and knocked it to the floor. "This him?" he said. "This him?"

"I used to be you," I said.

My stripper hobbled over on one heel, holding the broken shoe like a hammer. "Yep," she said. "Cheap ass fucker."

"I didn't do shit," I said.

Jeff jumped in, saying sorry and claiming we didn't know each other. Which, I realized, was true.

"If you don't know him," the bouncer said, "why the hell you sticking up for him?"

I bent over for my phone, and the stripper swung her heel on me and about punctured my damn eye out. I got yanked from behind and hit the floor. It was another bouncer. I could smell his cologne. They all wore the same stuff. I used to too. He was all over me. The cold metal cross of his necklace graced my cheek. Then he knelt on my head and mushed my face into the floor.

A bunch of people gathered around and I could feel the heat coming off them.

They were stepping on me and holding me down. Somebody talked into a walkie-talkie. "Don't move," he said.

"I ain't," I said.

After some deliberating, a couple bouncers picked me up and took me outside. The door banged shut and the lot went quiet. I didn't see Jeff's car. He must've bolted. I spotted where we were, the empty bottle.

I stepped out onto the blacktop highway. The sign on the building's roof was flashing, but other than that it was dark out here and the katy-dids were loud in the trees. I smacked my pockets. No phone, but still had my keys and my wallet.

I walked the highway back toward the lights of downtown. My truck was at the UPS docks. If I could just make it there.

I kept straight but ended up getting lost. I wondered who that dog belonged to.

I got sick behind a corporate tire place—or guess I did, because when I woke up there was a stinking patch of caked grass by my head. My cell phone was still not in my pocket. I was proud of myself for going toward the river, though, which put me probably no more than a half-hour walk from work. The tire place wasn't open yet, so I figured I still had time. I peeled myself off the chemical lawn and got going.

The street felt too hard beneath my feet, and the day too bright, even though it was cloudy. Walking back over the bridge, I got dizzy. There was a tugboat pulling a white line down the middle of the river, like a zipper.

I walked to the White's Truck Stop, the one with a Kathy's Koun-try Kitchen attached, went into the bathroom and washed my face and mouth. There wasn't a mirror, and that was a good thing. They knew their customers.

I took a stool at the counter, sipped coffee until it cooled, then told the waitress to fill the rest up with milk. "And give me a plate of eggs with grits and French fries," I said.

I held back the shakes while bringing the fork up to my mouth. Ate more than I could and there was still half a plate. She brought the check and I tipped her five bucks. Maybe it was possible to earn some good-luck points, a little bit of mercy. But I should've known that was wishful thinking.

My truck was where I left it yesterday evening. I got in and pulled the bottle out from behind the jumper seat. Just a little, to clear up the morning clouds. I turned the ignition, blasted the AC and sat there listening to my dad's radio station. The music wasn't playing, and he was off on a rip: ...*and you call this a free country! you hear? a free country! with all these faces on the TV telling you what you can't say and what you can't do...* The digital clock on the dash read 7:56. I checked my face in the visor mirror. That heel got me good on the cheekbone. I licked my palm and patted down my hair.

Breath was boozy, but no big deal. Ready for work.

Eddie, my boss, was waiting for me at the time clock. "Left your truck here overnight," he said.

I refused to talk to him without getting paid, so I punched my card before saying anything. "It wasn't starting," I said. "Jeff gave me a lift."

"But you just had it running out there," he said. "I saw you."

Jeff walked into the room carrying a white paper lunch sack. He lowered his eyes when he saw my face. "Gentlemen," he said.

"Thanks for giving James a ride last night," Eddie said.

Jeff's neck went rosy. "Oh," he said. "Yeah. We had us some fun."

"It's Sunday," Eddie said. "You're on forklift. You know that, right?"

"Yeah," I said. But the truth was, I'd forgot.

He walked me into the warehouse. I knew what was happening. The engine wouldn't start until you blew into the interlock breathalyzer. Legal stuff the company followed. I should've tried to talk my way out of it, but my head wasn't working. I just sat down like a big boy, pulled the mouthpiece free from the Velcro pad under the steering wheel and gave it all the fumes I had.

A little red light flashed and the device buzzed negative. I put the mouthpiece back without looking at Eddie. Just stayed sitting there.

"Come on, James," Eddie said. "You know what this means?"

"I know," I said.

"We got policies here," he said. "And this is one of them."

"I know."

"You know who's been calling?"

I put my hands on the wheel, felt the hard, round steering knob. The three lift levers—up and down, tilt, forth and back. I couldn't quit thinking about my operator's license and the picture on the wall hanging next to it.

"Go home," Eddie said. "Just go home."

I shouldn't have been driving. Red Thunder, me and her named my truck. I found it on Craigslist after my first few paychecks. Hundred fifty thousand miles for a couple thousand bucks. My little red Ranger.

Her phone was on the table in the kitchen when I got back. Then I heard the bedroom door opening, her feet in the hall. When she walked in, I could tell she was pissed.

"I was up all night," she said. "Where've you been?" She came over to hug me, then stepped back. "God, you stink of it."

"Sorry, OK?"

"What's that even mean to you? Like, you're going to change? Or you can't? Why haven't you been answering my texts?"

"I lost my phone."

"Well," she said, "let's find it." She picked up hers, tapped the screen and brought it to her ear.

I didn't want to hear that conversation, so I went into the bedroom. After a minute she came in. "Are you serious?" she said. "*Hindsight*?"

"It was Jeff's idea."

"Of course it was. It's never your fault. Somebody's always making you do something. This is exactly how it used to be. Poor you."

The hangover was in full swing and I was in no shape to argue. She shut the door on me.

My heart woke me up. The green circle was going. Another day gone. I reached for my phone on the bedside table, but then remembered.

Out on the kitchen counter was a note from her. I wasn't even about to read it. If she came back, she'd be leaving again just as soon as she heard about my job. And I'd go with her if I wasn't me.

Back at Hindsight, I spoke to a lady in the little front room behind the desk. It smelled like cigarette smoke and air freshener. "Yeah," she said, "We heard about you. They got your phone. Wait here."

Out in my truck I plugged the charger into the cigarette lighter and went driving. My brother joined the service because of what our dad always told us—*There ain't a lot of opportunity in this world for boys like you.* I used to not believe that, but the forklift license wouldn't be any good with UPS as my only reference. They took that shit serious. And I knew there wasn't much else I was good at.

Piggly Wiggly had a line of shopping carts in front of their entrance and employees were mopping the aisles. I parked my truck in the lot, turned on my dad's station, and got out the bottle. I watched everybody in there doing their little jobs. It got me thinking about how hard you work for nothing. A few more swallows led to an idea. I reached back and unlocked the safety case.

I drove around our block and the blocks surrounding it. I went up and down our street. After what must've been the fourteenth time, I passed our duplex, I saw her car was back in the driveway. I was trying to figure out how to make it all up to her, when I spotted my opportunity. My comeback. The thing that started all this in the first place. A guy in a hoodie standing outside her window.

I hit the brakes right there in the road. He didn't move. I took one last swig so I could follow through with it. He just stood there. I left my door open and went after him. He turned around and watched me coming, like he lived here. I shouted something. He pulled a pair of headphones down around his neck. "What's up?" he said.

I showed him what was in my belt. "Jesus," he said.

And I was on him before he could run. I grabbed his sleeve and pulled him in close. Exactly what I thought. One of the neighbor boys. I pushed the pistol into his stomach muscles. "So it was you," I said.

"The fuck?"

"This's a real gun," I said. "It's real. One that I paid real money for. That I worked a real job for."

"Don't," he said.

"It's registered too," I said. "The government knows I got it."

I heard her come out onto the front stoop. I turned and saw our duplex before the fire. Lights on in every window. Both halves whole.

"My boy," she said. But it wasn't Shelly's voice. And it wasn't Shelly.

The lady moved in between us with her eyes steady on mine. I couldn't look into them. She said my name, but I didn't know hers. She led her boy away from me. That's when I saw I was in the wrong yard. My place was the next one over.

Shelly came running. She saw what I was holding and stopped. "What's the problem?"

"Where you want me to start?" I said.

RANDALL KENAN
Mamiwata

for Dr. NCB

I've known rivers:

Ancient, dusky rivers.

—from "The Negro Speaks of Rivers," Langston Hughes

She took her time, walking like a fawn, careful not to make a twig snap. It was getting dark, but she could still see plenty. The voice grew and rose, and was the color of mint, like what Aunt Inez grew in a pot. Cool. Spearmint she called it.

She caught a glimpse of him, standing out in the middle of the creek, and he was quite a sight. Darker than she, with a wild head of hair. Big, berry dark lips. And his eyes seemed to flash in the dimming light. He was not exactly singing, more like humming, but in tune and to a rhythm foreign to her ears, yet familiar.

The water came up to his belly button, and he seemed to be doing nothing but standing there, in the water, humming and bathing, his dark skin glistening with water, and he spooned handfuls upon himself, humming his ditty.

"What you doing out yonder?" she called to him.

The man turned toward her with his flashing eyes and grinned in a playful fashion.

"Who you?" she said. "What you doing out there?"

"And who are you, little girl?" His voice was deep, deeper than Old Man Pharaoh's.

"I ain't no little girl."

The man waded closer to the shore, but stopped, and said, "How old are you?"

"They tell me I'll be ten and four come the next moon."

She stood on the shore, he stood in the water, for a quantity of minutes eyeing each other, she with curiosity, he with placidity.

"What you doing out yonder then?"

"Standing watch."

"What you watching for?"

"You possess a great many questions for a fourteen-year-old girl."

"Aunt Inez says I got gumption."

"I suppose you do. Do you like catfish?"

"Who don't?"

"Another question. Come back tomorrow and I'll have one waiting for you."

"Where you live at?"

"Wherever I take a notion."

She grunted. It was getting dark, and she did not want to be down there at the creek's edge in the dark.

"You better come outta there, son."

"Why?"

"It ain't safe."

"You think you're safe where you are?"

"Safer than standing in that black creek. Ain't you 'fraid of gators and moccasins?"

"Not really. Come back tomorrow."

With that she backed up, slowly, until her back came against a tree. She turned and dashed up the trail. When she got back to the camp, Aunt Inez was standing by the kitchen.

"Where you been, gal?"

"I seen a rabbit. Went a-hunting it."

"You aim to catch a rabbit bare-handed, gal? You ain't never caught no rabbit, why you rabbit-crazed today?"

"Seemed like a smart thing to do."

"Girl, I have told you time and time again not to stray too far from camp. Alone without menfolk with you. You never know how far them dogs and catchers will come out here."

"You and Uncle Pharaoh say they ain't gonna come this far into the swamp."

"Ain't no telling. We always got to be ready to run." Aunt Inez looked her up and down, taking her all in. Amanda could not tell if she was approving or disapproving. The older woman sucked air in through her teeth. "Go fetch me a pail of rainwater from that barrel over there, and bring me more wood, and be quick about it."

It did at this point occur to her to tell Aunt Inez about the humming, bathing man out in the creek, but when she opened her mouth to speak no words fell out. This worried her the way a mosquito bite worries. She went to fetch the water and the wood. She could smell the fish stew on the fire.

That night, her dreams were populated by dark men with broad shoulders emerging from the creek. They were not nightmares, but they left her feeling uneasy and querulous inside. And to feel curious things in curious places.

The next day, after a breakfast of leftover fish stew and cornbread—the crawdads were even sweeter the next day—she spent the morning splitting wood and weeding the corn rows. Aunt Inez sent her down to the creek to do some pot washing, with a cake of lye soap and a rag. She fully expected to see the man, but no man was there. All during her washing and scrubbing, she kept looking up and all about, but no man. Mandy felt the way she felt when Pharaoh didn't come back to camp after a visit back to the plantation. She lingered on the banks, but gave up, by and by, thinking hard thoughts of the well-made bather as she hauled the pots back to camp.

Rastus had caught a rabbit that morning, and Aunt Inez helped Mandy skin it. She allowed as how this was probably the rabbit she had seen the night before, a lie. Aunt Inez only moaned a moan neither in the affirmative nor in the negative, communicating that it did not matter one way or the other. 'Twas just the way things were. She now had another rabbit hide to tan and add to the quilt. Mandy loved to spend time rubbing her hand up and down the large tapestry of rabbit fur, black, brown, snow white, and mottled, so strong over you against the cold. Was a time she would feel bad for the murdered rabbits, but nowadays she got lost in the soft luxury of the thing. Plus, rabbits were good eating. She could not deny it. But the quilt reminded her of pretty things the Mistress owned back at Charybdis Plantation, expensive and lovely to the touch. Mandy did not like to think too much about the plantation. She reckoned she liked it better here. No. She did not reckon, she knew.

The sun commenced to go down, the shadows stretched out, and Mandy looked about for Aunt Inez, who was in the kitchen house, the smoke light as it tended to waft, and she snuck down the trail toward the water. A fat, long black snake crawled across the path a distance in front of her, and Mandy suddenly wished she had shoes, though she liked going barefoot when it was warm like it was. She heard the humming before she could see the water. She stopped stock-still. This time she decided to hide herself and fell to her knees and crawled into the thick cattails to the east of where the man bathed and hummed to himself.

He stopped humming. "Amanda. Why do you hide, child?"

Mandy stood up. "I ain't no child."

"But you are hiding?"

Arms akimbo, she asked, "Who is you, fool?"

The laughter was made of many things, and Mandy did not know what to think of it: Was he funning her, or was he just having fun? Was he happy out there, all wet and fixing to get et? Was he laughing because she called him a fool and he wasn't? It was a deep rolling laugh, the color of molasses, and his body shook. Ripples swam out from him in round, wavy circles.

He stared straight at her, bobbing up and down, lightly like a stick. "I am one of you." Now he was still and staring at her. "I promised you a fish, didn't I?"

It rose up behind him without sound, no water slurps or splashes, slowly. So beautiful it was, see-through and bright. Two round things, a point sticking up at each top. It was bigger than his head, wider than his shoulders, and covered the all of him like a great big oak bough full with leaves. The thing shone in the fainting light, the last rays of the sun danced on it like pixies or fairies. It looked like it was waving at Mandy, gently, as if in a breeze, but there was no breeze.

A holler came up in Mandy's throat, but no sound leeched out, only a puny grunt. And with that grunt the big thing flipped down into the water, made a scary loud SLAP against the flatness and went under. The water behind the man seemed to boil and rumble. Directly it came back up with force and direction, over his head. And right in front of her, with a loud, wet thud there wiggled the largest catfish Mandy had ever seen in her life. She ran. She ran hard, and stopped behind a catalpa tree, tall and skinny, but wide enough to hide her small frame. She was breathing rough, and her heart was beating harder than even the night of the fire and the raid when she was taken away from Quarters. That dark night full of flashes. Full of smoke and full of screams.

Mandy peeked out to see. The man was still standing there, grinning. The dog-sized catfish was still wriggling on the ground, its whiskers, each, looked longer than her legs; the mouth big enough to swallow her whole.

She struggled with it, carrying it in her arms, trying to avoid the whiskers, which looked mighty sharp. But it kept slipping from her grip and she kept having to stop to catch her breath. By the time she made it back to the catalpa tree, she'd stopped and looked back, but the fellow in the water had gone. Mandy felt angry with him. But was glad to be hauling back a big fish.

Aunt Inez was the first to see her clambering up the trail with a beast slipping around in her arms.

"Wheeooo!" Inez called out. Rastus came running and, much to Mandy's delight, lifted her slimy burden from her.

Uncle Pharaoh was standing there at the top of the trail. She knew what his return meant: he would commence to learn her the proper way to cypher and call letters as he did every time he returned to camp. Mandy was not exactly sure she enjoyed this reading and writing business, but she knew it was important to learn.

"You catch that fish, gal?" Uncle Pharaoh didn't look like he was either impressed or worried, just calm.

"Yes, sir, I did."

"Now, why the Sam Hill you want to lie to me, child?"

"I'll tell you the plain truth, Uncle. That there catfish jumped straight outta the water, right high. Just as pretty as you please, and landed on dry land. Right at my feet. I ain't even seen nothing to beat it."

Pharaoh grunted the way annoyed bulls sometimes grunt.

By now Rastus and Inez had nailed the catfish down to a board, hacked off its head, and commenced to peel back the thick hide, which Rastus had to put great effort into doing.

"I heard you talking to somebody out there by the creek earlier. Who was it?" Uncle Pharaoh asked.

"Just this fella, out there swimming."

"And you were gonna keep this a secret from the rest of us, were you? Was that your plan, Amanda?"

"No, sir."

"I assume he's a niggra like us."

"Yes, sir."

"He give you that catfish?"

"Yes, sir."

"It's a biggun."

Pharaoh joined Rastus and Inez, who were gutting the fish. "Looks like we got a friend."

"What you talking bout, Pharaoh?"

"Down by the creek. I prayed to her and she sent a friend."

"Now, there you go again talking all that African foolishness," Inez said. "Ain't nobody believing in them overseas magic people but you, old man."

"How you reckon that skinny little gal catch a catfish that big?"

Aunt Inez sucked her teeth dismissively. "Mandy, go fetch me some water, gal!"

Upon her return Pharaoh put his hand on Amanda's head. "You need to be on the lookout all the time, gal. Especially when you wander away from camp. I ain't gonna try to clip your wings or nothing, but I need you to tell me you'll be careful. You hear?"

"Yes, sir."

The next day, Mandy had been itching to go down by the creek since she woke up, but figured she'd wait till the dimming of the day just like the other times.

This time as she approached the water, she saw the man rise to the surface, head first. "Hey, Amanda."

"Hey yourself."

"Was the old fish good?"

"Sho nuff." Mandy found it difficult to look him directly in the eye today. "What was that yesterday? That thing you brought up out of the water?"

"That was me."

"What you talking about, 'that was you'? What does that mean?"

Of a sudden the man cocked his head to the side at a peculiar angle. "Ssssshusssh," he said, listening to Mandy did not know what.

"What's the— ?"

"Be still, child."

"Wha— "

Sternly: "I said, *Be still!*"

By and by, she heard, in the distance, the baying of the dogs. Hounds no doubt, and a great crashing not too terrible far away it sounded like.

"You need to come with me. Right now."

"I need to do what?"

"Don't be afraid, child. I will protect you." The man spread his big arms wide open. And Mandy felt herself impressed by how wide they were.

Pharaoh always said they were bound to be found out, to always be ready to pick up and run deeper into the swamp. The dogs were getting closer and she could hear the voices of the catchers, hollering. She figured she couldn't run back to camp in time. Besides...

"Come to me, child. Get in the water."

Mandy could hear the dogs louder, closer, crashing through the brush. She peered into the woods to see what she could see.

"Mandy. You must come now! Time is a-wasting."

Mandy was not thinking as she dipped her bare foot into the water and stepped in. Not too cool. Not cool at all. Warm like rabbit fur. Warm like a belly full of hot chicken. Warm like a freshly picked ear of corn. Warm like a ripe tomato. Warm like Aunt Inez's hands.

LOUISE MARBURG
Minor Thefts

The swimming pool was empty because there was a crack in its side that needed to be patched, so Emma used it as a hideout when she wanted to get high. Bundled up in her purple down parka and a pair of silver Uggs, she would squat on the cement near a moldy accumulation of damp leaves, hoping no one would see the rising smoke or smell the skunky odor of the weed. But the pool was thirty yards from her house, and half hidden behind a hedge; no one would think to look for her there—if they were looking, which they probably weren't. Her mother was busy getting divorced from her father, and her father had moved into an apartment near the train station. "My ex" was what Emma's mother called him to her friends on the phone, with a flat note of derision in her voice, though all of her friends had known him for years, and the divorce wasn't actually final. Once in a while, he would sneak back into the house when no one was home and take small but necessary things: a blender, a desk lamp; a marble cutting board for cheese. "Whatever, he can have it," her mother would say, but these minor thefts shocked Emma, the empty spaces where the things used to live. Why he took them was a question she didn't ask. She didn't ask either of them questions. No one would tell her the truth anyway, because even though she was fifteen, they acted as if she were a child.

One evening, her mother left the house in a cloud of perfume, her copper-colored hair done up in a chignon, her eyes heavily dosed with mascara. She returned at 10:30 with a strange man.

"Say hello to Doctor Feinstein," she said in a compressed, mincing voice that Emma had never heard. Gleefully, she clapped her hands together. "Doctor Feinstein delivered you, Emma!"

"What do you mean 'delivered me,'" Emma said, thinking of the Domino's Pizza guy who sometimes sold her pot.

"He delivered you into the world," her mother said. "He was my doctor when I was pregnant with you!"

Emma looked at Feinstein. He was much older than her father. His hair swept over his shining pate in lonely single strands. *You've seen my mother's vagina*, she thought. She shivered in disgust.

"You were a loud one, came out wailing," Feinstein said.

"How can you possibly remember?" Emma said.

"It wasn't so very long ago," her mother said.

"But he must have delivered a zillion babies since then," Emma said.

"You were memorable," her mother said. "I was in labor for thirty-seven hours."

Emma also doubted the truth of that because her mother loved to exaggerate. If she bought a bag of ten apples, she would call it a bushel; if it was warm out, she'd say it was sweltering. Probably she'd been in labor for half a day.

Emma went up to her bedroom but didn't go to sleep. She listened to her mother's trilling laugh and Feinstein's heavy footsteps. First they were in the kitchen—making drinks, she imagined—then they were in the living room, where their muffled voices rose up through the floor. She crept to the stairway landing to hear what they were saying.

"It was such a pleasure running into you at the party!" Emma's mother said.

"Delightful," Feinstein replied. "You were always my favorite patient."

"Is that so?" Emma's mother said. "I missed you when you moved to Baltimore, I didn't like my new doctor nearly as much."

"I wasn't crazy about Baltimore," Feinstein said. "Too hot in the summer. I'm glad to be back in Connecticut." But he was bored by retirement, he said, and lonely since the death of his wife. She said she felt liberated by divorce. He said she was as beautiful as ever. She accused him of flirting with her. That was exactly what he was doing, he said. Then there was a silence.

"My goodness," Emma's mother said. "What a surprise."

"I hope I haven't offended you," Feinstein said. "I couldn't help myself."

Emma leaned over the balustrade as far as she could, but all she could see were Feinstein's brown leather loafers next to her mother's rose satin pumps. They were sitting close together on the couch; the silence must have meant they'd been kissing.

"Gross me out," she said under her breath. Now she had *that* image in her mind.

*

Often, the kid who lived in the house next door joined Emma in the pool. His name was Montague Wandsworth, which Emma would have teased him about unmercifully if she hadn't known him since they were little. He was seventeen, and generous with his weed.

"My mother has a boyfriend," she told him the morning after Feinstein's visit. Monty nodded as if this came as no surprise. His parents had been divorced for years.

"What's he like?" he said as he squatted next to Emma.

"Old," Emma said. She decided not to tell him Feinstein had delivered her. "They were kissing." She pretended to stick her finger down her throat.

"So what," Monty said. "You and I kiss all the time." He tucked his shoulder-length hair behind his ears and produced a joint from the back pocket of his jeans. He gave it to Emma.

"That's different, we're young," Emma said. She lit the joint and took a long toke. "My dad's coming to pick me up in a while. You think I should tell him?"

Monty shrugged. "If it'll get you something."

"What do you mean?" Emma said.

"You're new to the parental divorce game," Monty said. "If you tell your dad there is a potential replacement for him, he might buy you something you want so he'll look better than this guy."

"He does look better," Emma said.

"He doesn't know that."

"I get it," Emma said. She wasn't going to play the game. Her father had been fired from his position as the chief executive officer of a conglomerate that made everything from light bulbs to fertilizer, and Emma knew from eavesdropping on her mother's conversations with her friends that he was having trouble finding another job. Her mother's only concern was how her divorce settlement would be affected.

Monty stood and walked over to the crack that ran down the side of the pool to the drain. "I think it's getting wider," he said as he traced his finger over its jagged path. Emma took another toke from the joint.

"I'm cold. Let's go over to your place," she said, letting the smoke drift out of her mouth. Monty's room was above his garage, separate from the rest of his house; his mother and stepfather had let him move into it as a seventeenth-birthday present. He and Emma had been having sex there nearly every weekend since then.

"I thought your dad was coming to get you."

"Oh, right, shit." She looked at the time on her phone. "Can I keep this for later?" she said as she tamped out the joint on the cold cement.

"Knock yourself out," Monty said, and slid another joint from his pocket.

Scrambling up, she pulled herself over the edge of the pool, skirted the hedge, and walked casually to the house. Her father's BMW was in the driveway.

Her parents were standing in the kitchen looking like they wanted to fight. Her mother smiled automatically when Emma came through the door.

"Daddy's here," she said.

"Where've you been, kitten?" her father said.

"Walking," Emma said gravely. "Thinking." While her parents gave each other bewildered looks, she tried to come up with what she'd supposedly thought about in case they wanted to know. Behind their backs, Denise, the housekeeper, winked genially at Emma. Denise had only worked for the family for about four months, after the housekeeper before her retired. At twenty-six, she was close enough to Emma in age that Emma considered her an ally. Denise knew that Emma had sex with Monty above the garage, and also that she smoked pot in the pool. Emma didn't have to hide her stash on the nearly unreachable shelf in her closet anymore, the way she did when their former housekeeper cleaned her room. Denise was pretty too, though her breasts were startlingly large, almost unsightly, making her look heavier than she actually was. Their former housekeeper had been a bony Estonian woman with a hairy black mole on her chin.

"OK, off we go," her father said, and they walked out to his car. Emma threw balled-up paper bags and wrappers from the passenger seat into the back before she got in. She smoothed out a bag and looked at it.

"Arby's?" she said. "Seriously, Dad? Since when do you like fast food?"

"Since lately," her father said as he pressed the ignition button. He backed the car out of the driveway, and turned into the road. "So, what's new with you, kitten?"

"Mom has a boyfriend," Emma said because she couldn't think of anything else. The weed was kicking in; the world went blurry when she moved her head. She turned on the element that heated her seat and dialed it up to high.

"She didn't waste any time," her father said evenly. "What's his name?"

"Feinstein," Emma said.

"Feinstein? Huh. She used to have a doctor named Feinstein. Years ago."

"That's him," Emma said.

"That's who," her father said.

"The guy. He was her doctor; Mom said he delivered me. Was she really in labor for thirty-seven hours?"

Her father gripped the steering wheel at ten and two, a minute muscle twitching beneath his eye. "Ridiculous," he said to himself.

"I know, right?" Emma said. "It probably won't last." She sat back and watched the familiar houses roll past, from enormous to merely big, until her father turned onto a busy four-lane road. It wasn't unusual for them not to talk while they were riding together in the car.

"No, she wasn't," he said.

"Who wasn't what?" Emma said.

"Your mother wasn't in labor for thirty-seven hours. It's pathological, the way she exaggerates."

"Oh, so that's why you're getting divorced," Emma said in a sarcastic voice. When they told her they were getting divorced, she hadn't needed to ask why. It was obvious they hated everything about each other; they fought like pit bulls in a cage.

Briefly, he took his eyes off the road. "I don't want to disparage your mother," he said.

"Oh, come *on*," Emma said. "You disparaged her every day when you were together. What, did you think I was deaf? I heard you screaming at each other all the time, there's nothing I don't know."

Abruptly, her father pulled the car over to a narrow verge by the road. He took hold of her shoulders and shook her like a rag. "You don't know a goddamn thing," he said. "You spoiled little brat."

"Let me go!" Emma said.

"Oh, Jesus, I'm sorry." He put his face in his hands. They were so close to the whizzing traffic that the car rocked in the wakes of passing vehicles.

"We can't stay here," she said. "Pull into that parking lot." He pulled into a Burlington Coat Factory parking lot and turned off the ignition.

"I'm going broke," he said to his lap. Emma thought he was going to cry. She felt around in the pocket of her parka and found the joint Monty had given her.

"Do you want some of this?" she said. "It might make you feel better."

He gaped at the joint as if it were a magic trick. "Where did you get that?"

"A guy," she said.

"You're too young to be smoking pot. It's not good for your developing brain. How long have you been smoking it?"

Emma thought a moment. "I don't know, a while. I'm fifteen, Dad. What were you doing when you were fifteen?"

"I smoked some pot," he admitted. "And did many other more wholesome things."

"I do plenty of wholesome things," she said. She was on the volleyball team at school, for instance, though she wasn't sure if he knew it. She took a mini Bic lighter out of her pocket and lit the joint. She passed it to her father. He opened his window and threw it out.

"I would lose all custody of you if your mother ever found out."

Emma sighed and pressed her nose against the cold glass of the passenger side window, fogging it with her breath. "We only see each other once a week," she said.

"That'll change when I find a job and get a place where you can stay overnight."

"OK," she said, though she didn't believe it. One afternoon a week was more time than she'd ever hung out alone with her father before her parents split up, because he'd worked such long hours during the week that all he wanted to do on the weekends was rest. She didn't believe he would find a job either, at least not very soon; many of her school friends' fathers were either unemployed or worried about keeping their jobs. A couple of kids had even been pulled out of Country Day and transferred to public school. She wondered if that would happen to her. She looked at her father out of the corner of her eye. He was staring straight ahead, hands on the wheel, as if the car was moving. Since they usually went to the movies on their day together, she asked, "What are we seeing today?"

He opened the car door, leaned out, and picked up the discarded joint. "Hand me that lighter, will you?" he said.

"What about your brain?"

"My brain stopped developing a long time ago." Holding the joint between his thumb and index finger, his other fingers raised, it looked as if he was signaling "OK" to someone outside the car. He leaned his head back, took a long toke, and blew the smoke in a thin stream against the car's ceiling, where it exploded into a cloud. He didn't offer Emma the joint, and for that she was glad. It was depressing watching her dad get high; he didn't look cool at all.

"My mom dated like twenty men before she met my stepfather," Monty said. "She went though them like chips."

Emma kicked off the bedclothes and looked down at her naked body, which had yet to develop beyond its initial pubescent sprout. Dim as a cave and overly warm, Monty's bedroom had the charm of a storage unit. There was his bed, his drum set, and a chest of drawers; most of his clothes were on the floor, emitting a faintly metallic stink.

"Did she sleep with any of them?" she said.

"A lot of them, yeah," Monty said. "I mean, I didn't like it, but I could see why—she wasn't going to marry some dork who was shitty in bed."

"Feinstein has been staying over a lot," Emma said. She disliked Feinstein more than she had anticipated. He talked to her as familiarly as her parents did, offering up random advice as if Emma cared what he thought. When she idly remarked that she didn't know how to play golf, he insisted on teaching her next summer; once, he suggested she brush her hair before the three of them went out to dinner. Her mother's voice had returned to its usual register, but she acted as if God had dropped Feinstein from heaven, making sure his favorite obscure craft beer was in the refrigerator and listening attentively to his every utterance. Emma imagined such behavior took a lot of energy, and hoped her mother would get tired of it so Feinstein would move on.

She sat up and reached for her underpants at the end of the bed. She liked Monty more than she liked anyone else, and had sex with him because he wanted to, but she had yet to understand why people thought sex was so great. He put his dick in her and pumped for a minute, yelped like a kicked dog, then pulled it out. She would have preferred they just fool around with each other's bodies the way they used to when they were younger.

"Are you going home?" Monty said.

"Yeah. Mom is actually cooking dinner."

"Where's Denise?" he said.

"Mom let her go. She said we can't afford a housekeeper any-more." On Denise's last day, she and Emma had exchanged email ad-dresses and promised to stay in touch. Not wanting to seem like an overeager pest, Emma was waiting for Denise to write first. "Mom's selling the house too," she said. "So, I guess I'll be moving soon." What about us? she waited for Monty to say, like a lover in a movie. When he didn't, her feelings were hurt—absurdly, she knew: rarely did anything she saw in the movies seem like it would happen in her life. "Hey, you want to come to dinner?" she said as she pulled her sweater over her head.

"No thanks," he said. "Nicole Hale and I are going to a comedy club in the city."

"A comedy club?" Emma said as if she'd never heard of such a thing. Nicole Hale wasn't beautiful but she was inexpressibly cool, and even if they didn't actually know her, everyone at Country Day knew who she was. Physically, she was the opposite of Emma: statuesque and dark, while Emma was ginger-haired, small, and lean. There was no reason Nicole Hale would know who she was, because though Monty was only a grade above Emma, they never interacted at school. Why didn't they? she wondered. Why hadn't she thought about it before? It was simply the way it had always been since the days when boys and girls publicly ignored each other even if they were privately friends.

She pretended the zipper of her jeans was stuck until she could compose herself. Her face was burning when she finally looked up.

"Sounds fun," she said. "Later, then."

Still in bed, Monty stretched his muscled arms above his head. "Yeah, later," he said through a yawn.

It was dark outside and the temperature had dropped below freezing; her boots crunched through a fine layer of ice on the snow as she crossed from Monty's driveway to her own. Though her eyes were swimming, no tears fell. She had never been a crier. The windows of her house were bright and warm, and all of a sudden she felt sad that she would be leaving the only home she'd ever known. Her mother was stirring something in a pot on the stove when she walked in the kitchen door.

"What are you gawking at?" her mother said. She wore a pink gingham apron that looked new.

"You," Emma teased. "Cooking."

Her mother blotted her forehead with the back of her wrist. "That's not fair," she said. "I've cooked for you and Daddy many times, and I make you breakfast every morning, in case you forgot. I used to cook dinner seven nights a week, you know, when your father and I were first married."

Emma sidled up to her and looked into the pot where gobs of meat and chunks of vegetables floated and bobbed in a bubbling greasy brown sauce. "When you were poor?" she said. Whenever her parents wanted her to know how lucky she was, they talked about the days when they were poor.

"Yes, then," her mother said.

"Are we poor now?" Emma said.

"No, of course not," her mother said. "What's the matter? You seem tired. Are you tired? Where have you been?"

"Around," Emma said. She laid her head on her mother's shoulder and breathed in her sweet, musky odor.

"My baby girl," her mother said. "Why don't you take off your parka?"

Feinstein came in from the living room. "Emma! How are you?" he said as if he hadn't seen her in ages. In fact, she'd seen him at breakfast that morning. He'd read *The New York Times* while eating his eggs, a swipe of yoke on his chin.

"Pour me a glass of chardonnay?" her mother said. Feinstein got her a glass of wine.

"Can we tell Emma now?" he said in the wheedling, baby-talk voice they sometimes used with each other.

"But I thought we agreed to wait until dinner," her mother said.

"Tell me what?" Emma said. "Tell me now." She hated being surprised.

Her mother put down the spoon with which she'd been stirring the stew, and took off her stiff new apron. "Doctor Feinstein, I mean David, and I— "

"Call me David, Emma," he said.

"David and I are engaged to be married," her mother said. She smiled broadly at Feinstein, avoiding Emma's openmouthed stare. "Isn't it fun? Isn't it just terrific?"

"It's terrific," Feinstein said.

"You can't be engaged if you're married," Emma said.

"Well, we can't be married yet, of course, but we can plan to be," her mother said. "The divorce will be final soon, anyway. Your father and I have reached a settlement."

"You've dated for, what, a month?" Emma said.

"Five weeks precisely," said Feinstein. He chuckled. "Though we *met* sixteen years ago."

"You were her gynecologist," Emma said. "Do you know how creepy that is?" She zipped up her coat and walked back out the kitchen door into the frigid night. Her mother pulled the door open just as Emma shut it.

"Emma, come back here this instant!"

"I'm going to Dad's," Emma said without turning around. She walked down the snow-swept steps.

"I'm not driving you to your father's," her mother said.

"I'm not asking you to," Emma said.

"You can't leave!" her mother cried.

Emma looked at her. "Why?"

"Because I say so," her mother said.

Emma walked away. She heard the door close. She knew her mother thought she'd be back in a minute. Looking up at the sky, she tried to choose one wish, out of all her wishes, to wish upon the evening star. She hadn't wished on a star since she was a child, before she learned that stars were merely planets reflecting the sun.

Her father's apartment building was less than a mile from her house, but she hadn't walked the distance before. She never walked anywhere—no one she knew did—so she felt conspicuous trudging beneath the streetlights along the suburban roads, cars whooshing by on the smooth tar, billowing white exhaust. The lights were on in the houses she passed: dim silhouettes of furniture and people, flickering television sets. She was perspiring beneath her parka, but her face was paralyzed by cold. She kept her hands in her pockets because she'd left her gloves on the kitchen table. She expected her mother to drive up any minute and demand she get into the car, but as car after car passed and didn't slow, she became determined not to turn back. Then, just as she was within sight of her father's building, a car did slow beside her. The passenger side window slid down.

"Hiya," said a man's voice from the darkness within. "You OK? Need a ride?"

"I'm fine," she said. "My dad lives right up there."

"Right where?" the voice said.

Emma pointed at the brick apartment building where her father lived. "The Greenwich Arms," she said.

"Come on, sweetie, I'll drop you off," the man said. "Get in, it's cold."

"No, I'm almost there," she said. The car stopped and the driver's side door creaked open. She didn't dare look at him.

"I'm Amos," he said. "What's your name?" None of your business, she wanted to say, but instinct told her to say a name, any name.

"Jennifer," she said. She stopped and turned as if she was going to get into the car, then pivoted and took off running. She heard only her own panting breath and the slap of her boots on the pavement. The cold air made her lungs ache. If she had to, she could identify the man. She'd seen him clearly in the half-second she'd turned. Small in stature, with a pale, narrow face, slicked-down mouse-colored hair, he'd worn a white shirt and a thin striped tie, a knee-length black coat, no scarf. Her father's building was a block away, then half a block; then she was there, pulling open the glass door to the wide, brightly lit lobby. The front desk attendant looked up in surprise. She whirled around and peered out the glass: the street was dark; the car was gone.

"Did you just see a car go by?" she said. "A silver sedan?"

"Nope," the attendant said. "Not that I was looking." He wasn't much older than Emma, a kid hired for a shift that nobody else wanted. He went back to the book he was reading. Emma walked over to the elevators and pressed the button between them. She leaned over, hands on her knees, and breathed several shuddering breaths. It was as if she'd dreamt the whole thing, the car and the man, his oily, cajoling voice. *Come on, sweetie.* Remembering it made her feel nauseated. She'd been so sure he was right behind her as she ran, snatching at the neck of her parka, but he'd gotten back into his car and driven off, and she'd been running away from nothing.

"There was a pervert out there," she said to the desk attendant, but he was engrossed and didn't hear. The walls of the lobby were pale mustard yellow; the marble floor was beige. She thought it was the bleakest place she'd ever been and wondered how her father could stand walking through it every day. The elevator doors opened and she got in. As it went up, the elevator made a skidding noise that sounded like it was scraping the walls.

On three, she got out and walked down a carpeted corridor that smelled strongly of roasting meat. 3A, 3B, 3C...different dinners were cooking behind identical doors. When she knocked on 3F, her father answered right away. He wore a green terry cloth bathrobe that Emma's mother had given him a couple of Christmases before, and held his wallet in his hand. On top of a small bookcase just inside the door, there was a blue-and-white china bowl, the size and shape of a pumpkin, that had sat on the front hall table in Emma's house for as long as she could remember. Her father must have taken it recently, yesterday or the day before, because she hadn't noticed it missing yet, and she would have, she always did. It gave her a start, seeing it here, so familiar yet out of place.

"Emma!" he said. "I thought you were the pizza delivery. What are you doing here? Your face is red, are you all right?" He moved to block her view of the apartment, but she had already seen Denise sitting on the couch. With her blond hair down around her shoulders and thick black makeup on her eyes, she was another version of the woman Emma knew, a recognizable stranger. She wore nothing but a plaid flannel shirt that Emma had seen her father wear on weekends.

"Hi, Emma," she said. Emma's father turned and frowned at her. "What? You want me to pretend I'm not here?"

"I was waiting for you to email me," Emma said. It was the first thing that came to her mind before she understood that Denise was having sex with her father.

"Don't cry, Emma," Denise said. "I'll email you tomorrow."

"I'm not crying," Emma said. She wanted to tell her father about the man who tried to lure her into his car. She wanted to tell Denise about Monty's betrayal.

She reached in and took the blue-and-white bowl. She would put it back where it belonged.

LYDIA MARTÍN
El Breakwater

The sun hadn't been up an hour when Angelina and Pablo Ramos tiptoed into the surf at Miami Beach, he sporting his ridiculous plastic nose guard, she in a petaled bathing cap, the rubber strap tight against her chin. The only sound besides the gentle wash of the tide was the fluttering of two seagulls settling on the water. They landed so close to Angelina that she froze, afraid to make a ripple and scare them off.

"Let's move here already!" Pablo said.

Angelina jumped and the gulls fled toward bleached pilings, their high-pitched *ha-ha-ha-ha!* like snide laughter in her ear.

"What else do we need besides this sea and these palms?" He was getting louder. "Why do we keep that apartment across the bridge? All those bills. All the cleaning you do. We should be on vacation all the time!"

Angelina teetered back toward shore, her bare feet finding every sharp rock and shell fragment. Pablo splashed along behind her.

They had been a couple for ten years, though they weren't married. The way they saw it, they'd never need to make it legal, because they already had the same last name. They'd met in Yonkers, when they were both in their early sixties. They took all their vacations to Florida, and as soon as they were able, they moved to Miami for good. They rented an apartment in gritty Allapattah, near enough to their daughters. Each had one; both had fled the north years earlier. And they continued to get away to Miami Beach, delighted that their regular oceanfront hotel was now just a taxi ride across a causeway.

"We can't live in a room for the rest of our lives. Be serious." Angelina dropped into her folding chair, driving it unevenly into to the sand. She sat lopsided, eyeing the horizon, pretending Pablo wasn't looming there, dripping and waiting for her to hand him his towel.

"I *am* serious." He reached for the towel himself. "I think I can talk el Breakwater into a discount. But we don't need to discuss the details now. Let's just enjoy this beautiful day."

"We don't need to discuss the details ever," Angelina said.

Pablo plopped into his chair and handed her the Coppertone.

"What do you want me to do with this?" Her gaze was still stubbornly on the sea. He pivoted to present his freckled back.

In 1977, South Beach was a tattered resort town, its glory days far behind, but Pablo and Angelina loved those invigorating waves. They were renting their favorite room at the Breakwater for the week and she just wanted to enjoy their daily dips in the ocean, their lazy afternoons in lawn chairs, sand underfoot, sipping icy pineapple sodas from the Styrofoam cooler.

"Do you realize how much cheaper the rates are by the month? Much cheaper than by the week," he said. "If we moved here for good, there would be extra money for you to spoil your granddaughter even worse than you already do."

Mostly, Angelina tuned him out when he started up. Mostly, he backed off. She had been clear that she wasn't interested in giving up their apartment just ten miles west, or in leaving behind the neighbors they'd only known a few years but who were like family—to her if not to him. It was beyond depressing, the idea of paring their possessions down to almost nothing in order to squeeze into one musty room with a leaky air conditioner in the window. She wasn't ready for the end, for the dismantling and contracting it required.

She worked the Coppertone into his shoulders, still strong like his chest, though now his chest was covered in a fine white down. She wiped what remained of the lotion on her knees and leaned back, hoping for a nap. If real sleep didn't come, pretending worked just as well. She had learned long ago that placating men, at least in the short run, could be achieved simply by clamming up. No point in saying the next thing, which would only lead to his saying the next thing.

"So what are you going to wear tonight?" Pablo finally said.

"My pink gown?"

"I guess that works for me," he said.

She'd take this as a truce for today. Angelina reached for a cold drink and noticed the slight tremble of her hands, and her cheeks suddenly felt flushed. Had she forgotten to take her blood pressure pill again? She replayed rising at dawn, tamping coffee down with a teaspoon, and setting the espresso maker on the blue flame of the tiny stove. The milk warming on the other burner spilled over just as Pablo opened his eyes. She had taken the time to scrub the stove after their café con leche and cornflakes. But yes, after that, she did line up her pills and Pablo's, and they'd shared a glass of tap water to gulp them all down on their way to the ocean.

They could afford to check into the Breakwater, with its optimistic streamline design, its broad front porch resembling the deck of a cruise ship, three or four times a year anyhow. Sometimes they stayed more often than that. When Pablo's tan started fading, when he glanced out of their apartment window and saw nothing but the parking lot, clotheslines drooping with boxers and bras and a few scraggly trees beyond that, he felt the call of those turquoise waves surging only fifteen minutes away and was insufferable until they made the next reservation at their hotelito.

Even the fancier rooms—facing the beach and big enough for a vinyl sofa the color of pea soup, plus a kitchenette with two folding TV trays tucked between fridge and wall—cost just $85 for a seven-night stay. Between their government checks and their respective bit of savings, they could pay their rent at home and have the beach too. Angelina wasn't ready, would never be ready, to live the rest of her days confined to a faded hotel full of shuffling retirees. Even if that hotel *was* just across the street from the Atlantic. God's Waiting Room, as the southern end of Miami Beach was called because so many old folks moved there, would have to keep waiting for Angelina.

It was Pablo's fault they had moved to the Allapattah apartment in the first place. They had dragged their winter coats, boots, galoshes, and gloves to the Salvation Army the day before boarding the last LaGuardia—Miami flight they ever intended to take, and as the moving truck made its way south, he limited them to looking for places in a part of Miami he now despised. Angelina had argued for an apartment in a quiet pocket of Little Havana, near her daughter, Soledad, and her granddaughter, Lena. But Pablo wanted to be closer to *his* daughter, Eneida, who lived just north of downtown, and he'd never budged from the idea that Eneida and her husband, who, after all, were childless, needed their company more. Never mind that Soledad was alone with a young daughter and could use a helping hand.

"Sole has her friends. And she won't waste time finding the next man," Pablo said. And Angelina had let him win.

They signed a lease on a bright one-bedroom that was twenty

blocks west of Eneida and her husband, Alex, the linebacker-sized telephone company engineer who never opened his mouth except to stuff something in it. The couple, in their mid-forties, seemed content with their bayfront condo and its starched staff at the door, and their constant trips to Europe. They were away more than they were in town. Pablo and Angelina saw them every couple of months, if that.

Their own building was a nondescript two-story with external hallways that flooded in the smallest rainstorm and was painted mustard and made even uglier by the iron bars over every window. There were six apartments downstairs, six upstairs, and the yard out back had a barbecue pit someone had put together out of cinder blocks, and a domino table where residents spent their weekends clicking tiles under the broken shade of a tamarind tree.

It was true that Allapattah was one of the grungiest neighborhoods in Miami. But it was also one of the few where blue-collar Boricuas, Dominicans, and Cubans, black and white, all managed to mix together. No snootiness. No divisions. They were all isleños, after all, born under the same kind Caribbean sun. Angelina could walk into any bodega, any dulceria or sandwich shop or five-and-dime and be greeted with, "Que tal, Doña?" Or, "Que lo que hay, mi vieja linda?"

Angelina picked at the loose threads of her flamingo-patterned beach towel while Pablo waded in and out of a calm sea. The business about moving or not moving remained on the tip of her tongue, but what she talked about was the solid blue of the sky, how balmy it was for the end of June, what she was craving for lunch.

"Maybe I'll order a big sopón marinero." Angelina drew Xs in the sand with her red toenails. "And a very cold beer."

"For me, the grilled grouper and yellow rice. But no beer. If I have one, I'll have two, and it'll make me too tired for tonight."

As the beach umbrellas multiplied, transistor radios blaring a tangle of rhythms, Angelina and Pablo swam, they sunned, they read the Spanish paper under the palms. Then they strolled to their usual Cuban greasy-spoon, where you had to yell to be heard over the festive racket of the crowd, something that always felt like being back in Havana to Angelina, but only rankled Pablo.

"Why do Cubans need to yell, even when they're just talking about the weather," he said as he took a sticky plastic menu, wiping it down with a wad of paper napkins before opening it.

By four, they were playing canasta with the others in the Breakwater's lobby. Angelina had to admit that she loved the Deco wall sconces, the clean block of the front desk made from keystone, always so cool to the touch. She loved the worn-out *I Love Lucy* furniture, the soft curves that reminded her of her living room in Havana. There was a familiar tropical dampness to this lobby, a hint of tart sea air that filled her nose and lungs and lured her into just sitting here for hours, like the rest of the old people did.

After the card game, Pablo and Angelina went up to their room for cool showers and Harry Reasoner, then a catnap to the clatter of the air conditioner. By nightfall they were strolling hand in hand to the Tenth Street Auditorium. She wore her full-length pink polyester gown, sleeveless for summer but with a high, ruffled neck. He was in a suit the color of wet sand and a shirt as pink as her gown. Their shoes were white patent leather. They knew they'd once again make mincemeat out of the old New Yorkers who thought they could mambo and cha cha. "Cha cha *cha*," Angelina would correct, whenever she heard anyone say it wrong.

"If we lived here, we could come dancing all the time." Pablo dug into his pocket for fifty cents, admission for two to the senior parties where four times a year there were heated dance contests. He and Angelina had accumulated a box full of ribbons, even for their foxtrot. But it was their synchronized Cuban stepping—hips and shoulders in play, instinctively breaking on two, moving in time with the clave but never, ever counting—that swept the others to the sidelines.

Angelina checked her fake lashes in her compact mirror. "We already come dancing here all the time," she tried to keep the edge out of her voice. "You've said it yourself, it's such an easy taxi ride, so pretty at night going over the causeway."

Benny Moré's silky tenor was coming from the speakers, over the scorching brass of the Perez Prado band. Pablo led Angelina inside and straight to the center of the dance floor, stopping under the mirrored ball that for once was spinning.

"Look at the king and queen of mambo!" cried Morris Sobol, who in his day played in the horn sections of Miami Beach's best ballroom bands. Now he was reduced to emceeing at the senior dances over his own record collection. "So pretty in pink tonight. Watch and learn, ladies and gentlemen!" He stepped off the riser to cut in on Pablo. "Señora Ramos, you're looking muy guapa tonight. Did you ever see Perez Prado's band live in Havana? I sure did. Listen to that brass! Tasty! I never took my wife to Havana. Do you know why, Señora Ramos?"

"How many times can you tell the same joke, Señor Murray?"

"Morris. But you can call me anything you like. OK, OK, I'll tell you. Taking your wife to Havana was like taking a sandwich to a buffet!" He howled at his own punch line.

Pablo was shuffling a retiree in a mod tangerine mini skirt across the floor. Leota, Angelina believed this one was called. She towered over Pablo, her crinkly thighs browned like a Thanksgiving turkey. After Leota came Adina. Angelina continued dancing with Morris, who had pretty good moves for an Americano and seemed almost as nostalgic as she was about Havana's heyday. He was going on about the baccarat tables and the cockfights when Pablo returned, just in time to take Angelina back for a swinging son montuno, the piano's tumbao too brazen for any of his groupies to follow.

"Cuba gave the world lots of good things," Pablo said as he twirled Angelina. "But none as good as you."

As they walked back to the hotel, the briny night air on their lips, he dropped an arm around her shoulders.

"Tell me this breeze is not delicious."

"No, it's delicious," Angelina said.

As Pablo leaned in to give her a peck on the lips, they spotted an ambulance inching down Ocean Drive. It stopped in front of the Breakwater. Angelina crossed herself as they stepped into the lobby ahead of two men in jumpsuits who fumbled with a gurney.

"It's Mimi. She's gone. Collapsed outside her room," whispered the Romanian widow who had moved to the Breakwater from Coney Island a few months back, right after she had put her husband of forty-six years in the frozen ground.

Mimi? Pablo and Angelina drew a blank.

"Oh, you know Mimi," the widow said. "Always painted her eyebrows on too high."

Angelina pulled Pablo toward the wobbly elevator. "No, no! Not another muerto being rolled out of here under a sheet! That's not the last thing I want to see before I close my eyes tonight."

But he sent her up alone. When he finally returned, almost an hour later, Angelina was in her nightgown, pacing the water-stained carpet. "What kind of vacation is it when there's always a chance of seeing a body coming through the lobby? What about the last one, the lady on the third floor who died with all those jars of urine in her room? Que horror! Que miseria!"

"What do you want? She shared a bathroom down the hall. It was a long walk." Pablo stripped down to his undershirt and boxers and started pulling back the flowered bedspread.

"And nobody to help her! Or even to notice she was so sick! Three days rotting in her room!" Angelina was barefoot, her face oily with night cream, her lashes stuck to a water glass next to the bed. "Death, death, and more death! That's what this place is. You can stay the rest of the week if you want, but I'm going home in the morning."

"Pero, mi amor," Pablo said. "They were sick. We still have time to enjoy life. We can leave in the morning if you really want to, but I was just going to tell you—while I was down there just now, the manager said there's a special. Two nights free if we stay until next Sunday!"

"Sí? What about Delfina?"

Sunday was their neighbor Delfina's seventy-fifth-birthday party and their building had a plan. Rosita and her husband were bringing helium balloons and party hats. If it rained, they'd be in charge of renting a tent, which they said they could get for cheap. The couple downstairs had a nephew who was a DJ and he was going to spin real merengue and bachata from Delfina's Santo Domingo. Half the neighborhood was coming. Angelina had volunteered to make big tins of arroz con pollo.

"We'll show up in time," Pablo said. "We can get arroz con pollo at one of those takeaway places. Why cook for two days? Nobody will know the difference."

Angelina dropped onto the vinyl sofa and looked out the window, at the sliver of moon, the sea so black she could only conjure the memory of it. "The building is expecting *my* arroz con pollo," she said, barely above a whisper. She started pacing again, fanning herself with a flimsy section of newspaper that did nothing against the heat on her face.

"I can't be here another day, much less another week," she finally said, grateful she had not raised her voice. "I'm finished with this place. Se acabó el Breakwater. You can stay if you want. I'm packing and going home tomorrow."

"Now you're being ridiculous. But, fine, go," Pablo said. "I'll see you next Sunday for the party."

Angelina departed at daybreak, in a taxi that Pablo insisted on hailing for her.

"Take some time and think about this," he said.

"The one who better think is you." Angelina resisted the urge to slam the car door.

From their first meeting, the Ramoses knew they'd be a couple. Angelina had been in the States for a year, after making good on a promise to leave Cuba the next time her husband raised a hand to her. Her brother Emilio, head janitor at a hospital in Yonkers, had sent money for the exit papers and the plane ticket to New York.

When she arrived at his little house on Buena Vista Avenue, he handed her an envelope with enough cash in it for her to buy a winter coat and boots, new curtains, a bedspread, and whatever else she needed for the bigger of the house's two bedrooms, which he had moved out of after his wife wasted away in there from cancer.

Dinner on the sofa in front of *The Lawrence Welk Show* became their Sunday night ritual. Angelina spent the day cooking oxtail stew until the meat fell off the nubby bones, fricasé de pollo with raisins plumped in cooking wine, caldo gallego with ham hocks, chorizo and turnip greens—and Emilio ate heaping bowls of whatever she made while he tapped his foot to the music. He would translate every word, Angelina's first English lessons. At the end of the show, they sang along with the Champagne Music Makers: "Good night, good night, until we meet again. Adios, au revoir, auf wiedersehen, 'til then!"

Pablo, who had lost his wife a couple of years earlier, happened to live in a boarding house two blocks up the street. The owners lived right next door to it in a smaller house; she was from the Dominican Republic, he was from Poland. Juanita Stronski, who had been close to Emilio's wife, cooked sancocho one day, borscht the next, and delivered it to the bachelors and widowers who rented rooms. She was particularly charmed by Pablo, who always wore a coat and tie and occasionally presented her with flowers and her husband with cigars, which he apologized for because they weren't Cuban. Juanita had looked the other way when Pablo brought in a hotplate so that he could make his own café con leche in the morning.

"There's a Cubano who rents from me," Juanita said to Angelina. "He came after his wife died, el pobre. I want you to meet him. Un caballero. And he has a decent job too."

The night they both came to dinner, Juanita made stuffed cabbage. Also cod fish fritters and arroz con habichuelas. Pablo showed up with two bottles of Rioja from the supermercado he managed. He wasn't tall, but he had a chin like Kirk Douglas and he wore a powder blue suit in honor of spring. Every time Juanita got up from the table to get something, he rose too. Every time she returned, he rose again.

"What do you miss most about Havana?" Pablo asked Angelina over flan and Sanka.

"I still think about those beautiful dances from when I was a young girl, the men in their white linen suits and those big orchestras playing danzones. What a paradise it all was before el barbudo turned it all to dirt."

"I wish I still had my white linen suit," Pablo said. "Then again, I'd look pretty ridiculous wearing it in Yonkers."

A week later, he called Angelina to invite her to a dance at El Club Cubano in New Jersey. "I'll make sure the band plays a danzón or two. My cousin and her husband have a car. We'll go with them so that I can prove my intentions are pure."

"I don't think I need a chaperona," Angelina said. "Remember I'm a grandmother." But she giggled more like a schoolgirl.

Soon, Pablo was coming over for Lawrence Welk suppers and singing along at sign-off. "Adios, au revoir, auf wiedersehen!" But he slept in Angelina's bed only when Emilio worked an overnight shift, and she always made him get up and go before her brother jangled his keys at the front door. Whenever they found cheap enough fare, they'd fly to Florida.

"I can't leave Emilio alone. Please understand," Angelina repeated whenever Pablo pushed for them to make good on their plan to move south someday. Then, five years after they had started seeing each other, Emilio fell dead in a hospital corridor, his floor buffer spinning off and crashing into the double doors that led to the emergency room.

*

Rain was pelting Allapattah when Pablo came through the door, his straw fedora soggy on his head. It had been a little over twenty-four hours since Angelina's taxi had left him standing in front of the Breakwater.

"The beach is not the same without you," he said.

Angelina threw her arms around him. She understood his desire to spend the years he had left loafing in swim trunks while the sun inched toward the Art Deco hotels, tinting them in pink and orange before dropping behind their parapets and spires. She understood that while everyone in Allapattah spoke the casual Caribbean Spanish that felt most like home to her, Pablo had lived in Yonkers since the early 1940s, abandoning Cuba not over politics but for an office job at the Domino Sugar Plant in Brooklyn. New York was where he'd picked up a taste for egg creams and sour pickles.

She knew he felt a kinship she never would with the Yiddish-favoring retirees who populated the washed-out hotels of Ocean Drive, that he loved going on capers with the guys, to dive for day-old dinner rolls in the dumpster behind Wolfie's and feed them to the seagulls, or to sneak into the Raleigh Hotel's famous scalloped swimming pool, where Esther Williams herself had kicked around once upon a time. They would arrange their folding chairs in the shade of the park that bordered the beach, where they could still hear the waves crashing, and whistle at the girls in bikinis who breezed by on roller skates and bikes.

But Allapattah's gente were nearly as chevere as Luyano's, the humble Havana neighborhood Angelina had turned her back on, fleeing not just from the Fidel Castro, who had dragged thousands of decent people in front of firing squads, but from the Fidel Castro under her own roof, the one she had married when she was much too young.

Just a few weeks ago, Angelina was walking home, lugging two grocery sacks, when one slipped and spilled, the sugar flying everywhere and her cans of pears rolling toward the gutter. One of the rough boys from across the street came running—the same one she had seen from her window, shirtless and sanding down to the bare metal a Chevy that Pablo said was likely stolen. He gathered the mangoes and the onions at Angelina's feet, fetched the cans of pears and wiped them clean with his bandana and then carried everything all the way upstairs to her apartment. He'd refused the dollar she held out but accepted a cold 7UP with a little bow. He called her señora, kissed her cheek, and told her to look for him next time she had too much to carry home from the store. "Me llamo Razor," he'd said.

While Pablo carried a heavy tin of arroz con pollo, steamed in broth and beer, down to the dusty yard behind their building, Angelina heaped a double serving of it onto a plate and walked it across the street to Razor, whose real name — she'd asked and he'd admitted — was Hilario. When she returned, someone had already strung the little flags, red, white and blue, from the trees. Now she only had to direct where the sunflower-shaped piñata should hang.

"Isn't Delfina too old for a piñata?" Pablo said. "What did you put in it? Geritol and Ex-lax?"

"No, chico, it's for the kids." Angelina swatted his shoulder. "So don't throw your back out fighting for the candy bars. I saved a few for you upstairs."

It had been a week since the flare-up on the beach and Pablo hadn't mentioned moving again. He nursed a rum and Coke as more neighbors showed up for the party. The man sure could charm. There he was in the short-sleeved shirt he'd pressed himself, mint green to go with his summer plaid pants, side-stepping with Delfina to one of her favorite merengues.

When the next bachata began, Pablo looked around for Angelina. He held her close and moved her slowly around the yard. And as night fell on Allapattah, she started feeling guilty for keeping him from his beach. She loved it too. Loved the sea air, the kind of hungry she got after a swim. Maybe she could talk him into a week at the Clevelander instead. It was a little more expensive, but there were usually lots of Cuban families from up north there. People with a pulse, people young enough to still believe life might stretch on forever. Pablo could visit his friends at el Breakwater all he wanted. It was just down the street. She'd propose it in the morning, after making his Cream of Wheat with condensed milk.

After the singing and the cake, Delfina, still in her party hat, threw her arms around Angelina. "Ay, mi amiguita del alma, I'm going to miss you so much." She wouldn't let go.

"What do you mean? Where am I going?"

"Pablo says you're moving to that hotel. When were you going to tell me? He was just asking if I would be OK with you coming back every now and then to stay with me. Of course! Of course you can stay with me!"

Angelina looked around the yard for Pablo, but he had already slipped upstairs. She found him in the kitchen, gulping ice water in his underpants.

"Did you say we're moving to the beach? Estas loco?"

"I didn't say *when* we were moving, mi amor. Calm down. I said we were considering it. I thought maybe if you could come back here whenever you wanted, we would both be happy. But enough with the back and forth. The truth is, I made a call to the Breakwater, and right now, if we pay a whole year in advance, we'll get two months free. That kind of offer won't come around again. It's time to act."

"Except we have a lease here and it won't be up for another seven or eight months. Or did you forget about that?"

"What lease?" Pablo refilled his tumbler at the kitchen tap. "We're month to month."

"What are you talking about? Since when?" The lease was her one real card to play.

"Since February. Since we decided there was no point in signing another lease because we were thinking about moving. Don't you remember?"

What she remembered was the day Pablo had insisted at the last minute that she go alone with Soledad and Lena to check out the new Omni mall downtown. Mother and daughter were on the way to pick them both up when he announced he'd have to stay home and miss all the fun. The landlord had called while Angelina was in the shower, he'd said. He was going out of town and wanted to come over right then to get them to sign their new lease. Pablo had negotiated month-to-month terms behind her back.

"You think you can just drag me to die in that place?" Angelina suddenly felt sick, and the tears she tried to conceal spilled anyway. She hurried to the bathroom and locked herself inside. She stood under a pelting hot shower until it went cold. Then she sat on the edge of the bathtub wrapped in her towel, waiting for Pablo to fall asleep before she came out. What could she possibly say to him now?

She remained mute the following day, well into evening. She cooked dinner anyway, because that was the job even of unofficial wives. But he'd have to live with fried eggs over white rice, her usual fuck-you meal. While the rice was simmering, she turned on the TV. The famous fat comedian from Argentina danced around bikini-clad showgirls balancing fuchsia headdresses. Pablo came to sit on the arm of the sofa.

"You know enough English," he said. "You don't have to watch the porquería on Spanish TV."

"I think your baseball games are porquería. But I don't bother you about it."

Pablo gave too big a laugh and offered to fry sweet plantains. Another attempt at a truce. But weren't they beyond truces now? When they sat down to eat, he cleared his throat, then he cleared it again. Angelina put down her fork. Maybe he was ready to apologize.

"You have six weeks to decide what we're taking and what we're getting rid of," he said in the puffed-up way her father and her ex-husband spoke when they were laying down laws. "I told the hotel we'd move in by the start of August. I don't want to hear another word. And I don't want any crying about it. I've been more than patient, and you've been nothing but stubborn. That ends now!"

Angelina stood. She sat again. She stared at her hands in front of her, so pale they hardly looked like they belonged to her.

"I'm not giving up this apartment," she said so softly it was a near whisper.

"Oh, no? Well, no woman is going to control my life!" Pablo pounded his fist on the table, making the dishes jump. Angelina's ex used to pound tables too.

A red heat spread across her chest and before she knew she was doing it, Angelina hurled her plate against a wall. Pablo's hands trembled when he stood, and he slammed the front door on his way out.

In the morning, Angelina woke to find rice and eggs drying on the wall and Pablo stacking shorts, socks, pants, and shirts across the length of the sofa. His favorite suits were draped over the La-Z-Boy.

"I didn't want to pull the suitcases out of your closet and wake you." He tucked a rolled-up belt inside his shoe. "I called the Breakwater. Only one room is available right now and it doesn't have the best view. But we can move to a better room later. You can take a few weeks to join me, if you need to. I'm going now."

Angelina padded toward the bathroom in fuzzy slippers, as if she'd heard nothing.

"I'm going with or without you!" Pablo yelled.

Angelina took her time showering and dressing, then she sipped her coffee standing at the kitchen sink while he finished packing. When she heard the taxi horn downstairs, she shut herself in the bedroom and blasted salsa on the radio so that she didn't have to hear him slam the door again.

A week passed. Then two. By week three, Angelina imagined Pablo in the clutches of one of the widows. Ora, maybe. Even under Angelina's nose she was always fussing over him, coming to the shore to present him with remnants of deli cream cheese sandwiched between saltine crackers. Was he teaching her to cha cha cha?

One afternoon, Soledad came to talk sense into her mother. "You know, he called me last night. He's waiting for you to change your mind."

Angelina already had to strain to recall the blue of his eyes. Early on, they had made her swoon. But they were eyes that monitored her all day long and still never quite saw her.

"I didn't leave two tyrants behind in Cuba to live with another one here," she said.

"Pero, Mami, what if he really won't come back? Pablo is not such a bad man. He's not my father."

No, Pablo was not Pancho. Pablo had never shown up drunk after a night on the town with God knows what floozy. He had never lost his paycheck at a card table, or busted her lip. But like too many Cuban men, Pablo insisted on wearing the pants. They always ate what *he* was hungry for. Went to bed when *he* was sleepy. Had sex when *he* was in the mood. He decided the weeks when they would go to the beach, even if Angelina had other plans. He even picked the clothes Angelina wore when they went out. And the time she came home from the beauty parlor with red hair, he had marched her back the same day and forced her to make it brown again.

"Did I tell you Delfina's cataracts are getting worse? She can't ride the bus alone to her doctors anymore. But we go together and we laugh the whole way," Angelina said. "And Rosita and her husband are having a baby. Won't it be nice to have a baby in the building?"

BOBBIE ANN MASON
Kittens, 1974

The day Judy had kittens, Carl Bernstein came to my house. The veterinarian had called it a hysterical pregnancy. Sometimes a cat will think she is pregnant and bloat up, but it's all in her head. The vet was so definite about this. Two of the kittens were white and one was a calico.

Carl Bernstein didn't seem to know much about kittens, and I was in a dither because I had four people coming to meet him.

I named the kittens Bilbo, Bubbles, and Alice. That was 1974, soon after Nixon resigned. Bilbo lived to 1995, just short of his twenty-first birthday, September 19.

I always remember the date Carl Bernstein came to my house, because it was the cats' birthday.

Judy had secured them in the small doghouse I had shoved under the porch. The doghouse was blue, with the name Max stenciled on it. Max had been hit by a car on New Year's Eve. I cried more over him than I did over my divorce, even though I hadn't wanted a divorce. It was unavoidable.

I lived in the country, alone. Friends tried to get me to move to town, saying it was dangerous to live out there in an old farmhouse after what had happened with Michael. "The Clutter family in Kansas!" they screamed. But the Clutters were a big family, rumored to have money, I protested. And I had a secret closet to hide in.

Carl Bernstein took a nap on my bed in the room with the secret closet. I imagined him finding the secret closet and hiding in it, just for the fun of saying "Boo!" From what I'd read, I thought he would be quite a cutup.

In the car from the airport, I had tried to maneuver him into telling me who Deep Throat was. I didn't know any better. But I figured out later that I must have offended Carl Bernstein. It was as though I hadn't understood Watergate at all. And Deep Throat's identity would have meant nothing to me.

Judy kept sneaking inside, flinging off her newborns. In the kitchen I had an array of cold cuts and some salad and unsliced bread from a bakery. There was pastrami, tongue, and roast beef. I didn't eat meat. I snipped off a bit of tongue for Judy, who was ravenous. I gave her milk and then, with a bowl of dry food, escorted her back to her sudden family. I told myself that I was not hysterical.

Carl Bernstein couldn't sleep. When the party began arriving, he trotted downstairs. I had invited a journalism professor and a political science professor. I had fetched Carl Bernstein at the airport and was responsible for getting him to his lecture. I had never done sophisticated entertaining before, and I soon realized that I didn't have enough cold cuts.

Carl Bernstein wanted more cold cuts and there weren't enough. For a moment, I considered Nine Lives liver pâté.

At his lecture that evening, about his Watergate reporting with Bob Woodward, the audience couldn't get enough. The questions went on and on. It had started to rain and I was worried about Judy. I planned to bring her and the kittens indoors. At a history professor's house after the lecture, the professor's wife offered Carl Bernstein coffee and the professor offered him some brandy. He said yes to both. I noticed that he got the coffee but the professor forgot the brandy. There was nothing to eat.

It was raining heavily, and the roads were slick. The history professor offered to drive Carl Bernstein to the airport, and I headed home. I drove slowly. If I ran into a ditch I might not be found till morning. I imagined a school bus finding my car nose-dived off a bridge into a creek, like Chappaquiddick.

Of course my divorce was nothing like Chappaquiddick, and Watergate seemed like an entertainment, a TV soap opera the summer of the hearings. Michael and I had watched the hearings devotedly, cackling over Sam Ervin's Southern humor and that hilarious "bagman," Tony Ulasewicz. John Dean's "cancer on the presidency" revelation drew us together. It was another jaw-dropping day when Alexander Butterfield revealed Nixon's taping system. Michael and I were as tight together as we had ever been, and I never thought we would part. In fact, we made love as soon as Sam Ervin gaveled the session to a close that day Butterfield testified.

I remember how Judy, who was a kitten then, scampered up and down the bed, purring and swishing her tail on us as we throbbed together, joining us, celebrating. We were laughing.

When Michael came up for parole, he sent me letters of apology. He still claimed he didn't know his embezzling spree was a Federal crime.

He wanted me back. I told him I'd think about it. I knew I would say yes if he could magically bring Max back with him. I said yes anyway because nothing since we split up had been even slightly better than crap.

Now we live in California! Life is jolly. We have a cat and a dog and enough scandals on cable to keep us going throughout our old age.

I see Carl Bernstein on CNN, all saggy and puffed and white-headed. And I wonder if he remembers going to a stranger's house the day a trio of unexpected kittens was born. All these years later, I am still thankful that I did not name the kittens Woodward and Bernstein. Some things you just know not to do.

DAN McDERMOTT
Ramtha

I'm fourteen and I ride a silver bike with knobby tires through a suburban landscape filled with cul-de-sacs. Fast as a mongoose. Jeans that
grip my thighs and ankles. Checkered sneakers. Black turtleneck and
a puffy, emergency-colored vest. The air smells like firewood because
every house has a chimney and every chimney is burning.

I bunny-hop a curb, launch off the Daltons' driveway entrance
ramp, fly four feet in the air, land in a wheelie and keep hammering the
cranks. Legs like pistons. Bionic legs. Head down. Handlebars rocking.
I know the route, don't need to look up. No one would dare jump in my
way. Frozen asphalt but no snow on the ground. A kind of winter-white
sky that erases the sun.

The Woods Road Fire Station sounds its baying siren and a truck
comes racing down Ardsley Drive bleating its pull-string horn. I cut in
front of the truck. Fast as a cheetah. I ride alongside and then cut back
and split the single-lane road. When I feel the engine's flat, warm face
on my butt I swerve left and launch off another driveway ramp—the
Phillipses' this time—and the firemen give me the finger and mouth
obscenities as they accelerate past. Dad says all the firemen are volunteers, flunkies, dropouts, and dope-heads. One of them has a face that
looks baked in oil. I hope he realizes that I let them win.

Mom moves into a new bedroom across the hall from her old one.
"Your father's snoring," she says, "is excruciating."

She has crystals on the window sill, a single bed, small box television
and VCR. The wallpaper is jungle themed: a loop of monkeys and lions
and bamboo stripes. Each monkey has a banana. Each lion is smiling.
Mom doesn't work, so she's able to chant until four in the morning.
Om, she says three thousand times while wearing a pyramid hat and
burning something that smells like chocolate. It's a school night, so I
walk down the hall and knock on her door and ask if she can pause
the chanting till morning. She whips open the door and scrunches her
blubbery gray face into a canyon of wrinkles and screams and screams

and screams and screams until I realize the screaming is worse than the chanting. My older sister, Phoebe, is in her bedroom. Dad is in his bedroom. The screaming must wake them but neither opens their door. The screams make Mom's head shake and the pyramid hat slides off to the left like a clock hand pointing to ten.

There's actually a house burning. This is not a test. The Palmers stand on their lawn watching the battle between water and fire. Mr. Palmer has a little arm that's bent like a chicken wing and pinned to his chest, some birth defect nobody's supposed to talk about. His wife has a nut-brown face and thinks women were made to wear dresses. They have two adopted sons, Adam and Luke, well-fed boys with clear tan skin and near-black hair who are real brothers and were adopted as a pair. Adam is my age and Luke is two years younger. Adam likes corny pop music. Luke eats his boogers. Their house is burning but nobody cries.

There are bookshelves in Mom's room that hold video cassettes instead of books. The woman on her video tapes has blond hair and a movie-star face. She sits in a throne and convulses until she turns into a man: baritone voice, bowlegged strut, smokes an invisible pipe and strokes an invisible beard. Channeling, Mom calls it. She says the man that the woman turns into is forty thousand years old, a warrior-king, named Ramtha, from the lost city of Atlantis.

Ramtha has followers who sit cross-legged on the ground in a barn atop Indian-style rugs. In some of the videos, Mom is sitting in the crowd and raising her hands and laughing and nodding and looking to the other followers whenever Ramtha says something poignant or funny. The barn is on a horse ranch on the other side of the country, in Olympia, Washington. Weekend retreats cost a thousand dollars, airfare not included, credit cards accepted. Mom has no money or credit but Dad thinks indulging his wife's new-age fixation long enough might get her to move back into his room.

The blond woman who channels Ramtha appears on *The Merv Griffin Show* and channels the ancient king in front of a live audience. Dad says the blond woman is a millionaire. He calls the followers Ramcrackers.

The dope-head dropout firemen seem to have given up on the fire. They stand beside the Palmers, holding red-handled axes with silver heads, watching the house burn. There's an ambulance in the driveway but no one to rescue.

Two summers ago, when the Palmers first moved into our neighborhood, Adam fell into the deep end of the Daltons' swimming pool. I watched him sink and scream bubbles before I reached in and pulled him to safety. I thought everyone our age could swim. Adam was raised with his brother in a New York City orphanage that couldn't afford a pool.

I tell my seventh-grade science teacher, Mr. Hall, about Ramtha and he says channeling is bullshit. Mr. Hall is six foot six and coaches the basketball team so he's allowed to curse sometimes.

I go home and tell Mom that Mr. Hall says Ramtha is bullshit and Mom says Mr. Hall is bullshit and when I return the next day and deliver Mom's retort Mr. Hall says, "Yes. That's sometimes true."

The Palmers' house is a charred black demon in our otherwise cozy-looking neighborhood. The chimney and a pair of half-melted kitchen chairs are the only things left standing. I can imagine a fireplace match slipping from Mr. Palmer's little deformed arm just after it's struck and the tiny flame feasting on the living-room carpet. I can also imagine Adam or Luke deliberately torching the place out of spite, retrieving one of the high-school kids' cigarette lighters from the school playground and using it to ignite the sitting-room curtains.

Screams from the Palmers' house used to penetrate walls and echo through the neighborhood. You'd hear the raspy mother. Then the barking father. Then Luke, scared and shrill and pleading. Then Adam, defiant and spitting and filled with *fucks*. Apparently, when the Palmers adopted the boys, they had the mindset of boxers looking for sparring partners.

Another of Ramtha's followers lives in a neighboring town and drives over to our house. She's close to Mom's age, almost the same height, same flaky alabaster skin, hair the same shade of gray, hiding a similar paunch beneath a too-big sweatshirt.

The other follower sits at our kitchen table and Mom serves pork chops and sauerkraut and glasses of soda.

"Ramtha saved me," the follower says.

Mom agrees, but I don't understand.

After dinner, I go up to Phoebe's bedroom and ask her what Ramtha saved Mom from. "I don't know," she says. "Dad's snoring, maybe."

Mom says the other Ramtha follower has a graduate degree in psychology. Mom dropped out of college to marry Dad, who was a senior when she was a freshman.

"You can't fool a therapist," Mom says of her new-age doppelganger. And when Dad disagrees, Mom adds, "Do *you* have a master's degree in psychology?"

And Dad admits that, no, he doesn't. She's got him there.

You have to drive fifteen minutes—out of our cul-de-sac, down Ardsley Drive and left on Hillsborough Road until it dead-ends at Highway 206—to make it out of our suburban neighborhood and into the center of town where condos are wedged together like Monopoly pieces.

You can walk to the Palmers' new condo from our middle school and Adam persuades me to cut gym class and shows me the bedroom he's forced to share with his little brother. A sliding accordion door with no lock, hardwood floors, one prison-style window too high to look out of, two single beds on opposite walls with a dresser between them. There's a Batman poster on one wall and a poster of pop star Tiffany on the other.

Adam shows me pornographic videos stolen from his father's wardrobe. We watch them in the living room but don't have to walk downstairs because the condo is only one floor. A different family, displaced from a different suburban home, I imagine, lives above them.

The video shows a courtroom. The judge has shiny red lipstick and golden hair. A mustachioed man pleads innocent, but the judge finds him guilty and takes him into her chambers and strips him down and lets him slap her butt cheeks red.

"Look at that bush," Adam says when the judge finally steps out of her thong.

*

The other Ramtha follower has a fifteen-year-old son who goes to private school and weighs like eighty pounds and has milky skin, pink eyes, and fine white hair parted in the middle and hanging to his ears.

"He looks like an experiment," Phoebe says. "Like someone sucked the life out of him."

Phoebe is sixteen and always says what she thinks. She and I both have fair skin dotted in beige freckles. We hold our arms up next to the follower's kid and feel better about ourselves. I've heard of albinos, but I thought it was something specific to tigers.

The albino's name is Kevin but we're supposed to call him Soap. The nickname started as Ivory, the kid tells us. Soap has been to Ramtha's Olympia horse ranch and taken classes at an extension school for kids. "They blindfold you," he says, "and make you walk through a giant maze. And they taught us to read minds."

I ask Soap what I'm thinking and he tells me it doesn't work that way. I tell him what my science teacher said and he says my mother is right: it's the science teacher that's full of shit.

Soap and his mother are moving to Washington to live on the horse ranch with Ramtha. He says it rains all the time, and he needs to get away from the sun. We're in the garage and he points at the ceiling.

"What about the blond lady?" I say. "What's she like when she's not Ramtha?"

Soap asks about my bike and takes a step forward and reaches for the handlebars before I can stop him. "Don't touch!" I say. "It's not a toy."

Adam and I get in-school suspension for cutting gym class and leaving school property. We're put in a room with no windows across the hall from the principal's office. We're the only two there. In-school suspension is rare. The room has yellow walls and carpeted floors and it smells like a urinal cake. People from the guidance office watch us in hour-long shifts—counselor, receptionist, cleaning guy. At eleven we're allowed to leave the yellow room and visit the cafeteria, but instead of taking our places in the lunch line, we sneak out the side door by the shop room.

Back at Adam's place the golden-haired judge is issuing another sentence, to a woman this time. The woman pleads not guilty and the judge orders her into her chambers where they both undress and lie one on top of the other with heads and crotches aligned. The guilty woman is darker than the judge and Adam says they look like a yin-yang.

We eat Doritos and drink iced tea in the kitchen. Adam takes a page from the *Hillsborough Beacon* and twists it like a pretzel braid and lights it with a flip-top metal lighter and leaves it burning on the table as we walk back to face the yellow suspension room.

I ask him if he's ever seen an albino.

"Once," he says. "At the zoo."

"I thought you were moving," I say to Soap. Our mothers are in my mother's bedroom chanting and burning chocolate and probably watching videotapes of Ramtha stroking his invisible beard.

"Next weekend," he says.

We're on the driveway. A cloud rolls by and exposes the sun and we move into the garage.

"Can't you wear sunblock?" I say.

Dad steps through the garage on his way to fetch the mail and stops to shake Soap's hand. "Well, look at you," he says.

I ask Soap about his father. Where is he? Is he also an albino? Is he also a Ramcracker? Is he named Shampoo?

He answers: *California, No, What's a Ramcracker?* and *That's not funny*.

He tells me his mother brought him over because she thought we might like to play together.

I tell him I don't like to play, not games and things anyway. I like to ride my bike. And the sun won't kill me.

"Video games?" he says.

I lead him to a Nintendo console in the downstairs guest bedroom and hand him a Mario cartridge and leave him there by himself.

"There are snacks in the kitchen," I say. "You probably like to drink milk."

Mr. and Mrs. Palmer are in the school guidance office waiting area. Adam and I are there too. Mrs. Palmer is in a dress and stockings. Mr. Palmer has a suit jacket with one sleeve hanging limp and the baby arm, his right arm, tucked in between his shirt buttons like Napoleon. My parents couldn't make it, because Mom doesn't drive and Dad can't get off work.

There's a police officer in the principal's office. The door is shut and the three of us are alone with the Palmers still waiting in the lobby with their adopted son.

They ask me if Adam started the fire.

I tell them *No* and then I tell them *Yes*. The *No* is a lie and the *Yes* comes after the officer tells me they already know Adam started the fire and I say then what the hell did they ask me for.

"He lit some crumpled newspaper," I say.

The principal says this is the second time in six months the Palmers have to look for a new home.

I tell them we ate Doritos and watched court TV.

Mom says I need to be nicer to Soap. We're going to be roommates soon. Phoebe is staying with Dad and I'm going with Mom and the follower and Soap to the land with no sun to live with Ramtha and enroll in the Ramcracker school for kids.

"Only temporary," Dad says.

"You need a change," Mom says.

"And we're getting a divorce," they say in unison, Dad then adding, "It's for the best."

They tell me I can't take my bike on the plane, but I say I can take it apart here and put it in a duffle bag and reassemble after we land.

Adam isn't there on my last day of school before leaving to live with Ramtha. *Reform school,* some of my classmates say. *Jail. Arson. Loser. Fuck-up. What's a Ramtha? What kind of name is Soap?*

A nosey girl who sucks the tips of her hair says Adam's little brother, Luke, was given back to that orphanage that can't afford a pool.

Mom and the follower had us stuff all our clothes in a donation bin in the corner of a supermarket parking lot. Ramtha has uniforms for his followers. Slip-on shoes with canvas tops and rubber soles, baggy cotton pants that leave your ankles exposed, burrito-wrap jackets that fasten with a cloth belt like my old karate gi. Crimson for adults, white for the kids. A gold patch is ironed on the shoulder once you reach the rank of Mind Master.

There are no horses on the horse ranch. Followers live in stables rigged with space heaters. Each stall is a bedroom. Mattresses stuffed with hay. An outhouse-style toilet in a shed. No phones. No TV. Community shower. All the apples and oatmeal you can eat. Sometimes Ramtha slaughters a calf and we kneel and pray and thank the baby animal for sacrificing its body. We have classes during the day and channeling lectures at night. The blond lady who channels Ramtha says Ramtha is glad I'm here, then she turns into Ramtha and he says the same thing in a slightly deeper voice.

Soap is one of three albinos as far as I can tell. Or maybe the other two are just really pale. It's hard to tell. Everyone is pale in this overcast place. Ramtha doesn't like the word *pale* and he replaces it with *pure*. The lighter, the better, he thinks. There are no people of color at the ranch. When Soap mentions his name, Ramtha strokes his imaginary beard and asks him to explain. Apparently, they didn't have soap 40,000 years ago.

On the first Saturday after we arrive, I dig my bike out of a barn full of personal items and assemble it in less than an hour. I fold my baggy pants into shorts and take off down the ranch's long dirt driveway and out onto the main road. A welcome sign says: RAMTHA'S SCHOOL OF ENLIGHTENMENT.

Instinct kicks in as soon as the tires hit asphalt. Born to ride. Legs like pistons. Fast as a mongoose. There's no traffic out and no one would dare jump in front of me. I could ride across the country in no time. *Escape!*

The rain falls as my legs pump. Fast as a cheetah. Perfect balance. No chance of wiping out. Suffocating pine in the air. Rain like pouring buckets. Cold rain, sharp rain, spewing from charcoal clouds low enough to scrape the treetops.

A house fire here would be out in a second.

EILEEN POLLACK
One a Day

1. Sweets

My father was a dentist, so I was allowed only one sweet a day. The reasons for this restriction were not mysterious. The water in our town wasn't fluoridated. When my father tried to convince his fellow citizens they should add this chemical to the well, they accused him of fomenting a Commie Jew plot to poison them. (Why else would a dentist want his neighbors' teeth to be so healthy they wouldn't need his services?) Every morning, I was required to take a tiny pink pill to make up for our lack of fluoride. But I still developed a mouth full of cavities. Visiting my father's office had its rewards. I was allowed my pick of the magic tricks in his closet. I got to play with the leftover globs of mercury. But I hated the whine of the drill, the nauseating jolt when it hit a nerve.

So I understood why I wasn't allowed to consume too much candy. The rule applied to my parents too. They didn't believe in bragging, but they were inordinately proud of their self-control. I never heard my parents disparage another family for their religion, race, or nationality. But they couldn't conceal their disdain for anyone who permitted their children to fall asleep with a juice bottle in their mouths or consume huge quantities of sugary soda, sticky candies, cookies, cake, or ice cream.

My parents grew up during the Great Depression. Having clawed their way out of poverty and, in my father's case, returned safely from World War II, they couldn't comprehend how drinkers, gamblers, adulterers, or profligate spenders could risk destroying the stability that allowed them to enjoy a clean, comfortable house and a healthy family.

As a child, I couldn't understand why anyone would do that either.

I remember my parents throwing parties only twice. With an elaborate flourish, my father would pour an ounce of whiskey in a jigger. ("Jigger," he kept repeating, delighted by the ridiculousness of the word.) In would go the ice and the whiskey sour mix. He made a comic show of jumping up and down to shake the shaker, then pouring the frothy cocktail in the glass. He popped in a maraschino cherry, and

I was allowed to take a sip. My parents couldn't imagine any child of theirs developing a taste for alcohol. But those whiskey sours were so delicious! How could anyone refrain from drinking them all the time? After the party, I went around fingering the cherries from the bottom of everyone's glasses and swallowing these on the sly.

Other than his weekly tipple of Manischewitz and those few whiskey sours, my father never drank. Yet, Christmas after Christmas, his patients brought him bottles of expensive scotch, wine, champagne, and fine liqueurs. These stood on the top shelf of our pantry, guarded by a ceramic soldier who held a urinous fluid called Galliano. In the thirty-five years we lived in that house, I never saw my father tap into anything except the whiskey for those whiskey sours and a flask of sweet Danish liqueur called cherry heering. (Given my family's proclivity for pickled fish, I thought the drink was called cherry *herring*, which is why I never sneaked sips, the way I sneaked sips of the Manischewitz.)

Apparently, in her more hedonistic days, my mother had smoked a cigarette. She still put out a fancy glass lighter and an ashtray for guests. But I don't recall the lighter containing fluid or the ashtrays being dirtied by any ash. My father owned a pipe. I remember him teaching me to clip the tip from a cigar. But he had spent too many hours staring into the dirty, diseased mouths of smokers to take up that habit.

When I was in high school, my parents were aware some of my contemporaries used marijuana. Once, my father noticed a patient's yellow teeth and asked if he smoked. The young man answered, "Only pot," which so astonished my dad he repeated the conversation at dinner that night, and the next night, and the next. "Only pot!" he kept repeating. "Only pot!"

That nearly every kid I knew was smoking dope, that some were shooting heroin or taking trips on LSD, while I took maybe two puffs on a joint my entire time in high school, earned me no credit from my parents. They simply assumed no child of theirs would be so irresponsible as to get hooked on drugs.

Don't get me wrong. There are worse child-rearing strategies than modeling self-control. The problem was, everything my parents taught me was a lie. They didn't *want* to do the things they refrained from doing. They hated the sensation of being drunk. Inhaling cigarette smoke made them ill. They weren't the type to shoot up heroin.

But they suffered as much as I did in trying to restrain their intake of sugar, fat, and calories.

In the pantry, beneath those unopened bottles of liquor, my mother maintained a constant supply of Tootsie Rolls, Twizzlers, Hershey's bars, and caramels. Usually, there was a big bag of marshmallows, which I would jam in my mouth two or three at a time, choking on the gluey glob; if no one was in the kitchen, I would jab a marshmallow on a fork and set fire to it on the stove.

My mother loved candy apples. We bought them in Atlantic City, or she made them at home by pouring molten red Karo syrup over each tart round Macintosh arrayed on a sheet of waxed paper, a stick jammed through the navel in each.

In the cookie drawer, my mother stocked Oreos (which my brother consumed in towering stacks when he got home from school), Chips Ahoy (which my father loved), and crumbly vanilla cookies called Lady Joans (the cookies were delicious, but the name irked me because my sister's name was Joan and I was always being chided to act more like a lady, like her).

In the baking drawer, my mother kept mixes for Bundt cakes, brownies, and Boston cream pies (my favorite). Before I was born, she made birthday cakes in the shapes of animals. I would stare longingly at the recipe book that described how to use toothpicks, coconut flakes, jellybeans, licorice sticks, and M&Ms to fashion lambs, butterflies, bunnies, and cocker spaniels, wishing she hadn't gotten tired of baking such masterpieces before I came along. Dejected, I consoled myself with the stale silver beads, sprinkles, and red-hot candies left over from those earlier projects.

Even in her less ambitious days, my mother baked us rich, moist, sour-cream coffee cakes, Toll House cookies from the recipe on the bag, and butter cookies, the dough for which she would pack into a metal cookie-press, changing the disc so she could crank out an amazing array of shapes. Once, I dashed into the kitchen between batches, grabbed a fistful of butter-cookie dough, then ran upstairs and sat in my own private heaven, nibbling that baseball-size gob of buttery, sugary dough for the remainder of the afternoon. To this day, eating that fistful of dough remains the epitome of culinary bliss in my life.

Perhaps bliss of any kind.

*

After her first coronary bypass, my mother ruthlessly avoided every milligram of cholesterol. But none of this stopped her from enjoying a fat-free slice of angel food cake, a box of bright pink Peeps, or an entire pan of Rice Krispie crunchies.

In the upstairs freezer, she kept the Cool Whip she used to make Jell-O molds (the Cool Whip tasted like machine oil, but I sneaked spoonfuls when she wasn't looking), as well as cubes of Hawaiian punch (my mother considered the juice to be fruit, so the punch-sicles were exempt from the one-treat-a-day rule).

In the basement freezer, I could always find ice cream sandwiches, Popsicles, Creamsicles, and Eskimo pies. By the garage door, the seltzer man left us beautiful beveled bottles of cherry and cream soda, which we drank with dinner because the laws of *kashruth* prohibited us from drinking milk with meat.

In the attic, where my grandmother lived, she kept a ceramic dish of chocolate kisses. I didn't really need to sneak those kisses; my grandmother loved me so much she would have given me the entire bag if I had asked. She had the sweetest tooth of anyone in the house. When I was six, she taught me to drink coffee with cream and three or four spoonfuls of sugar. (These days I leave out the cream, but I still heap in all that sugar.)

In the summer, when the Good Humor truck came tinkling around the block, my parents gave me money to buy a chocolate éclair, a chocolate-covered cone, or that crunch-coated vanilla bar that hid a solid chocolate core.

From a very young age, I was allowed to walk down the hill to the Dairy Queen, where, for a dime, you could get a vanilla cone, and, for another five cents, ask that it be dipped in a bath of molten chocolate.

On special occasions, my father drove us to Howard Johnson's for a dish of pistachio or butter pecan, a milkshake, or an ice cream soda.

Before a movie, my grandmother would buy me a box of Good & Plenty, Milk Duds, or Raisinets.

Our town used to be famous for its Jewish resorts, and we had a bakery so good that vacationers would load up on pastries to take back to Manhattan. Whenever we went downtown, my friends and I would stop at Katz's for a chocolate éclair, an almond horn, or a chocolate-covered cake-and-cream-filled pastry called a Liberty Bell (the name of our town was Liberty).

In the summer, I would visit the concession stand at my grandparents' hotel for a frozen chocolate-covered marshmallow bar and a bottle of Orange Crush. The hotel employed a baker whose job was to turn out trays of those colorful European cookies that taste of almonds and jam, as well as seven-layer chocolate cakes, Napoleons, cream puffs, rugelach, and who can remember what else.

On Halloween, hundreds of families would truck their children to my street, figuring the Jews who lived there would hand out the most expensive candy. So even though my father's professional career revolved around the scientifically proven fact that candy rotted teeth, we were responsible for pumping sugar into the bloodstream of a very high percentage of the kids in our town. Afraid of running out, my mother bought even more candy than she needed. Not to mention that my siblings and I would go around the block trick-or-treating. All of which meant we had another few big bags of candy to use up the rest of the year.

From September through June, my mother packed my peanut-butter-and-jelly sandwich with a Devil Dog or a Yodel. The high point of my day was nibbling off the hard chocolate shell that coated the Yodel, unrolling the cakey roll, licking off the icing, then eating the roll itself.

At three, my friends and I would stop at the gas station across from our elementary school to grab a snack on our way to Hebrew school. For reasons I no longer comprehend, I picked those vile novelties that contained colored sugar-water in waxy straws, fake cigarettes, and candy dots you bit off a backing of white paper, getting as much paper in your mouth as candy.

I also bought Bonomo's Turkish taffy, which would have caused my father to blow his top, if only because so many of his patients chipped their teeth biting into those plasticized bars. The trick was to smack the taffy against a sidewalk or a desk, shattering it into fragments. Hadn't the grownups listened to the commercial?

Give it a smack! Bonomo!
Give it a crack! Bonomo!
Lift off the flap! Strip off the wrap!
We're gonna taste Turkish taffy—hey, it's delish!
We're gonna taste Turkish taffy—answers every wish…

*

I doubt my parents snacked much during the day. But in the evenings, they had as difficult a time sticking to their rule as I did. Why else would my mother have kept us supplied with all those treats? I couldn't have been the only one making those boxes and bags of sugary snacks disappear.

My parents both had terrible teeth. My father had grown up at his parents' hotel, where he had unlimited access to the same cookies and cakes that later tempted me. By the time he became a dentist, the damage to his teeth was already done.

My mother inherited her sweet tooth from her mother. She loved anything made with butter (she even ate butter raw). Her father died when she was in her teens; she sank into a deep depression and her weight shot up precipitously. She thought no one would ever marry her. (Luckily, my father liked his women zaftig.) The only reason my mother slimmed down was that she loved being married to my father. Also, she suffered from an undiagnosed gall-bladder ailment that made her sick if she ate anything fatty. Heart disease ran in her family: her father and eldest brother both dropped dead of heart attacks; her two middle brothers and elder sister barely survived their own coronary woes. After my mother underwent the first of her two quadruple bypasses, she summoned all her self-control and avoided every molecule of cholesterol. She lived in terror of regaining the weight that had ruined her youth or dying of the heart disease that had felled her family.

Unlike other members of their generation, my parents knew how unhealthy sugar and fat could be. Yet, having survived their own impoverished childhoods and a war in which sugar and fat were rationed, how could they fail to find the plentitude of the 1950s and '60s to be irresistible? They prohibited us kids from consuming what tempted them. What shamed them. What frightened them. What threatened their self-control.

But in those days, parents didn't admit their weaknesses to their kids. They simply laid down the law.

Sadly, telling someone she mustn't have something, then surrounding her with that forbidden substance, is a very effective way to drive her nuts. As soon as I hit seventh grade and began to put on a few pounds, I was subject to remorseless scrutiny and humiliation. Because I felt so watched, I became conscious of every morsel I put in my mouth. I took to weighing myself two or three times a day. I bought one of those booklets that lists the calories in every food, then devoted 90 percent of my brainpower to figuring out how many pounds I might gain or lose by consuming what I was consuming.

When none of that worked, I invented what I thought was a unique method of maintaining a normal weight. If there's anything I remain ashamed of, it's all those years I spent binging and throwing up. Of course, I now understand the reasons I developed an eating disorder—the mixed messages about food I received from my parents; the unrelenting bombardment by images of sexy, thin women; the ostracism by my classmates, who made me feel lonely and odd because I loved reading books and studying science; the scorn heaped on any girl who enjoyed kicking or hitting a ball, running a race, jumping a hurdle, or even jogging. Most pernicious of all, no one talked to me about what might constitute a satisfying life, other than getting married and having a child who wasn't allowed to fall asleep with a juice bottle in her mouth or to consume too much candy or cake.

But it's still hard to believe I spent so many years doing something so stupid and injurious to my health.

Not until graduate school did I cure myself of my bulimia. I didn't do this by exerting some magical form of self-control. I simply developed more satisfying ways of spending my time than eating. Instead of taking in sugars and fats, I gorged on novels, essays, stories, ideas, and poems. I saw a therapist. I made new and better friends. I purged myself of my anxiety and rage by writing. I played tennis. I lifted weights. I jogged. I practiced the piano. No one put limits on what I ate. No one watched. No one tried to shame me. I stopped eating so much because everything else in my life became so much more pleasurable and fulfilling.

That, and I started to have great sex.

2. Sex

I'm sure all sorts of biological, social, and environmental factors contribute to eating disorders. But I am equally sure people who have found a satisfying way to earn a living and who enjoy regular sex with people they love are more likely to resist addictive behaviors than people who hate their jobs and spend their evenings and weekends alone.

In my mid twenties, I met a kind, brilliant, handsome man. We fell in love. We had sex. In fact, we had far better sex than I'd had with anyone.

We had sex in sailboats. In tents. In meadows in the high Sierras. We had sex in our tiny attic apartment, which could be reached only by climbing three rickety flights of outdoor stairs. We had sex in my Republican in-laws' guest room in Houston, Texas. We had sex in my childhood home. And in my parents' retirement condo in Boca Raton, Florida.

On our wedding night, we had sex in a fancy hotel overlooking the Charles River in Boston; in the middle of the night, hungry and exhausted from so much sex, we found a hundred-dollar bill in one of our wedding cards and used it to order room service, which neither of us had ever done, and ate crab cakes naked on the floor.

On our honeymoon, we had sex in a Finnish sauna. In a cramped bunk in a ship moored in a Stockholm harbor. In a cheap boardinghouse in Copenhagen after a night searching for an X-rated movie, because we had heard that Danish porn was the sexiest in the world. (I'm sorry to say I don't remember what film we watched, or even if we found a theater.) On that same honeymoon, we had sex in a German train inside a ferryboat, with guards pounding on our door, yelling *"Herauskommen!,"* and demanding to see our passports. We went skinny-dipping in a stunningly blue pond amid the glaciers high in the Norwegian fjords, then hiked to the hut where we would be spending the night and had sex before the other hikers got there.

After our honeymoon, we had sex in our marital bed in Cambridge. We had sex in a ski chalet north of Montreal, where we got snowed in for three days. In southern Spain, after stuffing ourselves with tapas, imbibing too much sangria, and sneaking into the local bullfighting ring to see a flamenco competition, we had sex and conceived our son.

After that, we pretty much stopped having sex. But I loved kissing and hugging my son and rolling around with him on the floor so much I hardly minded. Besides, I was too busy teaching, writing, cleaning the house, doing the laundry, shopping, and cooking to find time to eat. I lost so much weight my mother kept telling me I was too thin and urging me to eat.

Even after I left my husband, I managed to have great sex. Not sex with a lot of men. But a lot of great sex with the few men I loved.

I think the reason I'm not screwed up about sex the way I'm screwed up about eating is my parents didn't send conflicting messages about sex the way they did about food. Having grown up hanging around with the comedians at his parents' hotel, my father constantly told dirty jokes, even with his five-year-old daughter at the table. Where I grew up, sex wasn't shameful or sinful, it was funny. Sex was sexy. Sex was human. Sex was one of the reasons that life, with all its *tsuris*, was still worth living.

My mother often told my sister and me about her own sister advising her before her wedding night to "just close her eyes and get through it." But my mother didn't think that sounded right, so she went to the library and found a book that offered better advice as to how a woman could enjoy sexual relations with her husband. Her message to my sister and me was clear: we should enjoy having sex, just not with someone we didn't love and weren't married to.

As a result, I never felt I was being told to abstain from a pleasure everyone else was indulging in on the sly. I didn't feel watched. I didn't feel shamed. I wasn't constantly being told not to want—or even think about wanting—something I wasn't supposed to have.

3. Solitaire

Not long ago, I got dumped by someone I truly loved. I moved from the Midwest to Manhattan and suffered a series of terrifyingly bad online dates. I retired from teaching. I still had my writing to keep me occupied. I made new friends with whom to play tennis or go out to eat. But I found myself with far too much time on my hands. I began to grow afraid of getting old. Of never again having sex.

So I shouldn't have been surprised my obsession with food crept back.

Here I was in a city whose restaurants serve the best food to be found anywhere in the world. American food. Chinese food. French food. Italian food. Thai food. Malaysian, Ethiopian, Middle Eastern, Korean, and Japanese food. To get from the subway to my apartment, I have to pass a pizza place that serves, if not the best pizza in Manhattan, then a pretty good runner-up. If I dodge the pizza place, I need to hurry past a joint called Koko Wings, whose specialty is double-fried soy-garlic chicken strips that call to me like the Sirens singing to Odysseus.

Instead of shopping for ingredients and cooking dinner, I simply point to that night's selections amid the rows of delicious prepared foods in the glass case at the West Side Market. Or Fairway. Or Citarella. Or Eataly. Or I stop at one of the taco trucks that dot my neighborhood. I struggle not to order a fruit tart from the Silver Moon Bakery. Or a chocolate bapka from Zabar's. Or a slice of strudel from the Hungarian Pastry Shop. Or a thick wedge of caramel pecan cheesecake from Café Lalo. Or a cupcake, cronut, muffin, or chocolate truffle from any of the boutique vendors on every block.

At sixty, I'm too healthy and sane to binge and purge. And yet, to keep from eating, I watch episode after episode of my favorite TV series. At first, I needed to make up for having been too busy with my career to watch *Breaking Bad, The West Wing,* or *Arrested Development.* Given that I was now living in Manhattan, I needed to rewatch every episode of *Seinfeld, Sex in the City, Saturday Night Live,* and *30 Rock.* Then I moved on to *Orange Is the New Black, VEEP, Transparent, Inside Amy Schumer, Unbreakable Kimmy Schmidt, The Great British Baking Show, Project Runway,* and, purely for sociological reasons, *The Bachelorette.*

I even started watching porn. I'm not addicted to porn. But that's only because most porn is so misogynist. That, and my computer crashes no matter which site I try. Still, I have come to understand why so many men—and, for all I know, women—spend so many hours watching porn. It's right there, on the computer you're trying to use for work. By definition, it's so seductive.

I find it impossible to stay off my laptop. Whenever I get stuck writing—which is every few minutes—I check my email. Then my Facebook account. Then my Twitter feed. I watch movies on Netflix. I watch *Modern Family* and *Black-ish* on Hulu by using a password I stole from my cousin's husband. I use that same password to watch tennis on ESPN and Chris Hayes and Rachel Maddow on MSNBC.

I am so addicted to computer solitaire I can't start writing in the morning unless I have won a hand. Or another hand. Or another. I play solitaire on my iPhone while I'm watching Netflix or Hulu on my laptop. I force myself to go for a walk in the park, only to find myself sitting on a bench to check my email, then my Facebook account, then my Twitter feed. Then, as long as I have my phone out, I play another round of solitaire.

Not long ago, I gave in to the urge to click on one of the ads for a game called Panda Pop that kept appearing on my phone between hands of solitaire. I vowed I would play only the free sample. Then I downloaded the app. Now I am far more addicted to Panda Pop than I ever was to solitaire. How can I let those poor baby pandas suffer at the hands of the evil baboon? How can I watch the panda mother cry if I don't save all her babies?

Solitaire is a meditative game. I can calm myself, even think, while I play it. Panda Pop is far more frustrating and rewarding. If I fail to save all the babies, I feel terrible; if I pop a cascade of bubbles and the babies come parachuting down and the panda mamma claps and smiles, I am flooded with an adrenaline high. Even when I'm not playing, I see bubbles ricocheting around the margins of the book I'm reading or the screen of the computer on which I'm typing. It's all I can do to finish this paragraph before giving in to the urge to pop some more bubbles and save another batch of baby pandas.

4. Pot

Most of the behaviors to which I am addicted aren't dangerous. Sometimes, they provide much-needed relaxation. But living in a constant state of vigilance, fighting everything I am tempted to indulge in, makes me feel so crappy and full of shame I obsess about the behavior I just engaged in, which makes me want to engage in it yet again. I keep thinking: Is this really how I want to spend my remaining years on this planet? Is this what the human race evolved to do?

The truth is, nearly all of us now live in a world that's as crazymaking as the house I grew up in. Even as we find ourselves surrounded by more and more stuff that's engineered to be irresistible, we are constantly being lectured to refrain from giving in and consuming it. Often, we are being told this by doctors who are obese, or government officials, celebrities, or members of the clergy who are addicted to drugs or porn. Our children are being ordered to put down their phones and turn off their iPads by parents who can't tear themselves away from their own phones and iPads.

Unlike the candy in my mother's pantry, the flashing, buzzing games, the television shows, the social media accounts, the porn sites, and the YouTube videos that tempt us today exist in limitless quantities within devices we can hold in our hands and whose buttons we can push twenty-four hours a day, with no one looking. Never before have human beings been inundated by such craftily persuasive advertisements, brought to us via media that are impossible to avoid and as addictive as the products they are selling us. Entire magazines and television shows devote themselves to seducing us into desiring the finest gourmet foods and the richest, trendiest desserts. If I found it so hard not to put on weight in a house where my mother served boiled chicken and frozen green beans for dinner, in a town where the only ethnic offerings were chop suey and pastrami sandwiches, in an America in which dark chocolate hadn't been invented, how are our children going to resist all the carefully formulated snacks and delicacies that have become so plentiful, even as we adults go on and on about how vital it is to avoid sugar, fat, gluten, salt, and artificial additives?

We caution our children not to binge on alcohol, even as we extoll the virtues of the finest wines or artisanally crafted beers. Smoking pot has become so acceptable that even a woman of sixty like me keeps an entire bag of weed in her fridge. (If the SWAT team breaks in, they will never think to look in the Tupperware container in the crisper drawer.) Kids know their parents—even their grandparents—smoke pot. The rule seems to be they can relax with a few puffs themselves, as long as they're careful not to smoke so much they can't get into Harvard.

Then there are all the antidepressants, mood stabilizers, anxiety relievers, attention focusers, sleep inducers, opioids and other habit-forming pain medications that are being pushed on us by our physicians, therapists, and television sets.

It's hard to imagine what effect this is having on our children. All the mixed messages. The constant need for vigilance and self-control.

We have all read that children who can delay eating one marshmallow now because they have been promised two marshmallows later are more likely to succeed than the losers who lack the discipline and restraint to wait. But has anyone ever studied how to instill willpower in a child who lacks it? Has it ever occurred to anyone that the child who eats one marshmallow now rather than two marshmallows later is going to end up healthier?

5. Nutella

As an infant, my son was so overweight strangers stopped me on the street to berate me for overfeeding him. On his pediatrician's orders, he went straight from breast milk to skim. Even so, he remained obese. He didn't walk until he was eighteen months; he was so heavy I could barely carry him. When I sent my mother a professional photograph of her grandson, she ripped it up and urged me to do the same with the other copies.

For his first three years, I made sure Noah didn't eat anything sugary or fatty. He thought Halloween entailed dressing up in a costume and handing out bags of raisins to the other kids. Then I realized I had become as obsessed with controlling my son's diet as my parents had been obsessed with controlling mine.

After that, I tried never to make a big deal about what he ate or how he looked. I didn't stock a lot of sweets in the house, but on special occasions, I baked cookies or a cake, or we would take a walk to the Dairy Queen to celebrate. When his friends began spending hours playing *World of Warcraft*, I bought my son a few video games for his own computer. But I also tried to make sure he got outside and found other pastimes that absorbed him. He loved watching *Rugrats, Rocko's Modern Life*, and *The Simpsons*. Often, we laughed at these shows together. But we also had plenty of talks about what he might do with his life that would bring him more satisfaction than watching TV.

Now in his twenties, my son stands six feet two inches tall and weighs little more than he weighed in grade school. He jogs. He rides his bike. He boxes. He is studying for his doctorate in history, a subject he loves, and devotes most of his free time to organizing for social justice. I don't want to violate his privacy, but let's just say I raised him to think of sex as a vital part of a healthy romantic relationship. He exhibits little interest in sugary snacks, alcohol, drugs, or social media. Until recently, he lived in a co-op where I never saw anyone chow down on anything more decadent than a whole-wheat muffin.

In fact, when I visited him at his new apartment—a single room in a converted funeral home in a drab, working-class neighborhood in Chicago—I thought I might have raised a kid who has too much self-control. When I offered to treat him to dinner at the restaurant of his choice, he drove us to a modest Uzbeki restaurant. When the waiter offered us dessert, my son declined.

Sadly, I still craved a bedtime snack.

Well, Noah said, he did have something sweet squirreled away in his pantry. He took me into the kitchen he shares with his housemates, stepped inside the closet, and emerged with a half-eaten jar of Nutella and a barely opened package of graham crackers.

"You like Nutella?" I said.

"I love it," he admitted.

We settled at the grimy Formica table, spread the former on the latter, scraped the jar clean, and—guiltily, happily—demolished the pack of crackers.

RON RASH

L' Homme Blessé

Every month, there were two or three phone queries like this one. Some-one had bought a Monet at a yard sale in Weaverville or found a Gre-cian urn in a woodshed. One deranged caller claimed he'd discovered the missing arms of the Venus de Milo. Others wanted him to evaluate folk art, hoping some elderly relative might be the new Grandma Moses or Howard Finster. A few showed up at the college unannounced, treasure trove in hand, sent by a receptionist or administrator to him, Brevard's only art teacher. Most could be persuaded to seek evaluations by muse-ums or galleries, though sometimes, out of personal curiosity or their insistence, Jake agreed to examine what they had. If nothing else, the consultations fulfilled his department's community outreach require-ment, which would help next year when he came up for tenure.

This time the art was too large to bring to campus, which meant a twelve-mile drive to an isolated farmhouse, but it was an excuse to miss his afternoon office hours, which so late in the semester meant students either arguing or begging for higher grades. Besides, the caller was Shelby Tate, whom he'd taught two years ago. A good student—smart, serious, a bit older than most. She'd mentioned the paintings in class one day when they discussed folk art. Her great-uncle had cov-ered every wall in his bedroom with painted portraits of strange beasts, her comment garnering odd looks from the other students. Jake had planned to go see them during the semester break, but what happened to Melissa changed all that.

Jake locked his office and walked to the faculty lot. Across the way, a grounds crew decorated the administration building with white Christmas lights, a reminder to get his prescription refilled. The de-tailed directions to the farmhouse allowed him to cut off the GPS, so he spread them on the passenger seat and headed west on Highway 19. The leaves were off the trees now, revealing time-worn swells so unlike the wild, seismic peaks and valleys so beloved by European Roman-tics such as Pernhart and Friedrich. Sturm und Drang. Yet the Appa-lachians were daunting in their uniformity, a vast wall, unmarked by crevices that might provide an easy path out.

When the odometer neared twelve miles, Jake watched for the red realty sign marking where to turn. Gravel first, then dirt leading to a bridgeless stream. As the car splashed across, a back wheel spun for a moment before gaining traction. The woods opened up and a small house came into view, most of its white paint peeled off, the tin roof pocked with rust. A red Jeep Wrangler was parked in front of the porch. Shelby came out of the house to greet him. Although she wore sweat pants and an oversize sweatshirt, her pregnancy was evident. There was something else too, that he'd either forgotten or not noticed before. Her eyes were the same light blue as Melissa's had been.

"You have any trouble finding the place, Dr. Yancey?" she asked, her accent more noticeable than he remembered. "Matt, my husband, says I'm not much good with directions."

"No, they were fine."

"I'm sorry to call you so sudden but we got a buyer yesterday for this place and things are moving pretty fast. We'll be closing on the sale soon."

"It wasn't a problem," he answered. "It gives me a break from listening to students complain about grades, something you never needed to do. You made an A, I recall."

"Yes, sir, I did," Shelby answered, and hesitated. "I wasn't certain you were still at the college, but I'm glad you are."

For a few moments, neither of them spoke.

"Well," Shelby said, nodding toward the open door. "What I wanted you to see is inside. Watch that first porch step, Dr. Yancey. It's so rotten it might give way on you."

A lantern was beside the door and Shelby struck a match and lit the wick.

"There's no electricity." She said.

He followed her into the front room. As his eyes adjusted to the muted light, Jake saw dusty pieces of furniture, a fireplace holding a few charred logs. They walked through a small kitchen and then down the narrow hallway. Shelby paused at a door on the left.

"In here, Dr. Yancey," she said, raising the lantern as they entered the room.

Strange beasts, indeed, Jake thought, his gaze drifting across the walls. The images were amateurish but discernable. A zebra with red spots instead of stripes, a small spiked fin on its back, a shaggy elephant with down-curving tusks, a deer with the snout of an anteater, a thin-legged boar. Plywood had been nailed over the room's single window frame, on it in calligraphic black the face of a lion. Except for a moldering mattress on the floor, the room was bare. But as Jake's eyes adjusted, the animals became a bit more naturalistic. A mastodon, not a hairy elephant, a bison, not a boar. Despite the fin, the spotted horse, too, was familiar.

"I've seen these images before," Jake mused aloud.

"Where?" Shelby asked.

"A book on ancient art. They were inside a French cave."

"A French cave?" Shelby asked, clearly puzzled. "That seems so unlikely."

"Why?"

"How would Uncle Walt know about paintings like that?"

"Same as me, I imagine, from an art history book."

"But he didn't have any art books."

"Then television."

"Uncle Walt didn't have a television, and once he got back from the war, he hardly left this place except when my grandfather took him to town twice a month to cash his Social Security and VA checks. Grand-daddy told me Uncle Walt always tended to keep to himself, but after coming back from World War II, he was a lot more that way."

"When did he paint these?" Jake asked.

"Right after he came back from Europe."

The images did appear that old, the red and black paint flecked, the lion fading into the warped and rotting plywood.

"When did he die?"

"2001."

"Did he paint any besides these?"

"Not that I know of."

"So during the war, he was in France?"

"For a while. They sent him back home before the war ended," Shelby said and nodded at the animals. "I used to think maybe it was what he saw in his nightmares, but if it was, why did he sleep in here all those years?"

"Did there used to be a bed in here, not just a mattress?"

"No, just the mattress. When I was a kid and we came to visit, Uncle Walt let me jump on it, like it was a trampoline. A couple of times, I got spooked being alone back here, so I'd go back out front with the grown-ups."

"Folk-art dealers would find these interesting," Jake said, "but the wall prints are so faded, and trying to get them out without the plaster crumbling…"

"I figured that, but it's not why I asked you to come," Shelby said. "Before we sold the land, I wanted someone besides his kin to see the paintings, someone who might appreciate his doing them."

"I'm glad you did."

"I'd like to think it helped him," Shelby said softly.

"Maybe it did," Jake said, more emotion in his voice than he'd wished. He pulled out his phone. "I can show you some of these images right now."

"There's no reception out here," Shelby said, and smiled, "which isn't always a bad thing. I get a few whiners about grades too, not the students but their parents."

"What grade?"

"Fifth," she answered. "Most of them are real sweet and I'll miss them when I'm on maternity leave."

"Do you mind if I take a couple of pictures?" Jake asked.

"No," Shelby answered.

He took one of each wall before putting the phone in his pocket.

"I'll compare them when I get back to the office. Maybe he saw photographs of them in France, if not in a book then a magazine or newspaper."

"I guess that's possible," Shelby said.

They looked at the walls a few more moments. The images were not originals like the wild bestiaries of a folk artist like Richard Burnside, nor was there some stylistic quirk. More like something copied from a book by a talented child, he thought, but as he stared at them Jake was moved that the man had felt such a deep need to express what he'd endured. They walked up the hallway and onto the porch. Shelby closed the door but did not lock it.

"I hope everything goes well with the pregnancy," Jake said. "I'm sure it will."

"Everything's fine so far."

"Good," Jake said. "If you give me your email and phone number, I'll let you know if I find out anything interesting about the paintings."

"Sure," she said, writing down the information and handing it to him.

"Thanks for showing the paintings to me," Jake said, and paused. "And thank you for the card you sent after Melissa died. I should have responded but, anyway, this visit allows me to thank you now."

Shelby nodded and pursed her lips. "I almost didn't call. This is probably a hard time of year for you."

"Well, I'm glad you did call," he answered, and got in his car.

Jake recrossed the stream and was soon on the two-lane back to Brevard. The name of the cave lingered just on the edge of memory. Not one word, like Lascaux or Chauvet, but two words, one starting with a P. He was driving slowly and several cars and trucks passed him when the road straightened. As he neared the Brevard city limits a Subaru wagon came up fast behind him, tied to its roof a Christmas tree, its tip pointed at him like a spear. A black tide of memory washed over him.

December 14, almost exactly a year ago, he and Melissa had been decorating for a Christmas party, three other couples invited. It had been a good afternoon. Jake's grades were posted and Melissa's campus counseling office had just shut down for the holidays. Melissa had gotten a promotion, and Jake's division had told him that his chances for tenure were excellent, so there was much to celebrate. They had gone all out: holly on the fireboard, a Fraser fir wreath. They'd even made an iTunes mix of their favorite carols. Melissa had been setting the table when the forks slipped from her grasp and clattered against the floor. She placed a hand on the table to steady herself and told Jake she was dizzy. A day later Melissa was dead. In the hospital room, he had lifted her hand, the forearm rising too. It felt heavy and cold, like clay.

Shelby was one of two students who sent a card. There had been nothing special about it, one likely picked up at a CVS or grocery store, the card's sentiment followed by a handwritten sentence about his being in her thoughts and prayers. A brevity Jake appreciated, especially when others had said too much. He'd been amazed at what people, intelligent people, could utter at such a time. An English professor, his own wife beside him, quoted Tennyson's "better to have loved and lost, than never to have loved at all." Another colleague had said "it's good you two decided not to have children," and yet another told Jake that at least he was young enough "to find another wife and start over," as if Melissa were simply a defective machine part easily replaced. What allowed Jake to hold his tongue was the realization that at some wake or funeral he might have said something just as insensitive.

When he got back to his office, no one else was around. Jake left the lights off, the only glow that of the computer screen as he tapped in **cave art France**. After a few clicks, the bison, mammoth, and lion appeared. The spotted zebra was there too, though it was actually a horse. What Jake had thought a fin was was instead a human hand hovering over the animal. Pech Merle was the cave's name. He pulled up an article about its discovery in 1922. Black-and-white photographs showed the first scientists exploring the cave.

When they were in grad school together, Mason Bromwich had chosen cave art as the subject of his dissertation, so Jake typed a message noting how the paintings were identical to those in Pech Merle, adding that the man who'd done them was in France during World War II.

My question is this, Jake typed. **The cave's images would be in French magazines and newspapers at that time, correct?**

He didn't expect an immediate reply and was about to shut off the computer and leave when Mason's response came.

Hi, Jake, Long time, no hear. Re paintings—by details, you mean even the colors are right?

Yes. Jake typed. **Orange bison, red dots on the horses.**

Give me a few minutes, ok?

Jake leaned back in his chair and waited. Footsteps came down the hallway, a familiar clack of heels. Jake was glad his office light was off. If not, Lila Marshall would stop and want to chat. She'd recently gone through a divorce and felt she and Jake were kindred spirits. There are worse ways to lose your spouse than through death, she'd once told him. Lila's office door opened but soon closed again. Her heels echoed hollowly back down the hall and she was gone. Mason's response finally came.

Your soldier didn't see them in a magazine or newspaper. The best sources I know of say no color Pech Merle photographs before 1951, even in art books, much less newspapers or magazines. (That's in France or anywhere else.) The only way to know all those details would have been visiting the cave itself. M

Jake typed a response.

I doubt he'd be wandering around in caves. They were fighting a war, you know.

Then someone's lying about when the images were painted.

I don't believe the person's lying, and the paintings appear that old.

I could be wrong. Maybe color photographs were taken, but a GI coming upon them? It's a stretch, pal. Check troop movements. If anything they might have passed through the area.

Thanks for the help.

No problem, Jake. You doing okay?

I'm okay.

Janice and I would love to have you come up here for Christmas.

Thanks, but I'll just stick around here.

Okay, but if you change your mind...

Okay. Got to go. Thanks again.

Jake sat back in the chair. A set of research papers lay on the desk waiting to be graded, but the thought of doing them was overwhelming. Going to the pharmacy the same, or getting gas for the car. So he stared at the blue screen and its icons, and when that disappeared he stared at the dark.

Moments or minutes later, he could not say, there was a dazzle of light.

"Sorry, Professor Yancey," Mabel, the night custodian said. "I didn't know you were in here. I can come back later."

"No," he said. "I was just about to leave."

Jake sat a while longer, summoning the energy to get up, to walk to the lot, to turn the key in the ignition. The gas could wait but not the prescription, so he drove to the CVS. Inside, Christmas reds and greens dominated, but holiday cheer was absent at the pharmacy. It was near closing and the employees looked tired and harried, the customers much the same. The young woman just ahead of him, Kleenex pressed to her nose, appeared especially miserable. The store's harsh fluorescent lights seemed designed to heighten such unhappiness. If you don't stay, you won't sleep tonight, he told himself.

But then the customer at the counter turned and dropped her prescription into a gift bag decorated with candy canes and green stockings, stirring memories of a Christmas stocking stuffed with candy canes, but also with tangerines and, at the bottom, two boxes of crayons. He must have been four because he wasn't yet in kindergarten. Jake remembered the crayons' waxy smell as the colors and shapes flowed unmediated from hand to paper. The wonder of the act had never left him. Not even now, he supposed, thinking of the menagerie on the wall.

The woman in front of Jake paid, one hand holding the tissue and the other a white prescription bag. Jake stepped to the counter. After he got the prescription, he made a couple more purchases before leaving. Get the gas while you're out, he told himself, and stopped at a convenience store. Once home, he ate a sandwich, then dialed Shelby's number and told her what he'd found out.

"He did the paintings in 1945," she said. "I'm sure of it. The paint cans are still out in his shed. I bet they'd prove it."

"I'm not doubting you or your family," Jake said, "but my friend says the only explanation is that he was in the cave. Did he ever talk about anything like that?"

"I never heard of it, but I can ask my daddy and call you back."

"Sure, I'll be up till at least ten."

"It probably won't take but a minute," she said.

Jake hung up and poured a glass of wine. The message light flashed on his landline phone. He checked the number and saw it was his sister. She wanted to know if he was coming to their parents' house for Christmas. Perhaps it would be better than last year when family and neighbors acted as if he'd arrived cloaked in a black pall.

As he poured a second glass of wine the phone rang. It was Shelby.

"Daddy said Uncle Walt never talked about the war or France to him, and hardly to my grandfather either. But there was a man who'd been in the same unit. He'd come over sometimes to see Uncle Walt. Daddy said he was at the veteran's home in Asheville the last he'd heard. I checked and he is. I was thinking about going over there Saturday morning." Shelby paused. "You'd be welcome to come along."

Jake had no plans for Saturday morning, other than a faculty luncheon at noon he'd just as soon miss.

"OK," he finally said. "What time?"

"Ten all right?"

"Where do you want to meet?"

"How about at Uncle Walt's," Shelby said. "It's easier to find than my place."

"Sure," Jake said. "And could you ask your father if he knows which division your uncle was in?"

"Sure. He's got Uncle Walt's discharge papers, so that's easy enough. Daddy's likely gone to bed, but I can find out tomorrow."

"That will be fine," Jake said.

As Jake finished the wine, he again scanned the internet for images of the cave, finding some that were not on the bedroom wall, including one of a bison but also a man. The French phrase below intrigued Jake, so he opened the link and expanded the image. The human figure was leaning, perhaps even falling, and vertical lines passed through the torso. Jake read the article, which suggested several interpretations based on mythology, shamanism, the image's coloration and location within the cave. He shut down the computer and took the Ambien. As always, he awoke around three, feeling a tightness in his chest as he lay in bed. He knew he wouldn't go back to sleep, so he made coffee and waited at the kitchen table for dawn to lighten the window above the sink. He showered and dressed, then drove to the college to teach his last classes of the semester.

On Saturday morning he arrived at the farmhouse on time, but it was 10:20 before Shelby showed up.

"Sorry," she said. "I stopped to pick up some baby clothes from my sister."

"No problem," Jake said. "I can drive if you like."

"No, I like driving, especially while I still can without my stomach pressing the steering wheel. Plus, I know a shortcut to 40."

Jake got in the Wrangler, baby clothes and a white pastry box on the seat between them. Shelby splashed across the creek and soon they were on backroads Jake had never traveled.

"Have you met the man we're visiting?" he asked.

"I was at Uncle Walt's once when he came but he probably won't remember me. His name is Ben Winkler."

"He must be in his early nineties."

"Ninety-one, Daddy said."

Shelby slowed and turned again. A sign said Ashville twelve miles.

"Last night, I researched troop movements through France," Jake said. "As far as I can tell, your uncle's division didn't pass anywhere near Pech Merle."

"You know, I thought about something else this morning. What if there was a color *painting* of the cave, and Uncle Walt saw that?"

"I hadn't thought of that."

"Well, if there was one, maybe Mr. Winkler saw it too."

After a while the road curved sharply, the baby clothes sliding against his side.

"I can put those in the back if you like, Dr. Yancey," Shelby said.

"No, they're fine," Jake answered, looking more closely at the clothes as he pushed them back toward the center. "So you're having a boy?"

"Yes," Shelby said.

"Have you decided on a name?"

"Brody. It's a family name."

"Brody," Jake said. "I like that."

Shelby started to speak, then halted.

"What is it?" Jake asked.

"You and your wife," she said slowly. "You didn't, don't, have children?"

"No," Jake answered. "We were still discussing whether to or not."

"Oh," Shelby said, the single vowel softly lengthened.

At the retirement center, they signed in, and the receptionist pointed to the elevator. "Fifth floor. Take a right. It's room 507."

The door was open. Mr. Winkler sat in a recliner in the corner, a folded newspaper on his lap. A metal walker stood in front of the chair, tennis balls on the legs. After they introduced themselves, Winkler removed a pair of black glasses and set them and the paper on a lamp table. He rubbed the paunchy flesh below his eyes a moment, then motioned toward two plastic chairs. Shelby set the white box on the room's single bureau before sitting down.

"Pull those closer," he said. "My hearing's not what it used to be."

Jake and Shelby moved nearer.

"So you're Walt's niece?"

"Yes, sir," Shelby said. "Grand-niece, that is."

Jake introduced himself. For a few minutes Shelby made small talk with Mr. Winkler, asking about his health, the family pictures on the bureau. Her manner was unhurried and respectful. Though only thirty-six, Jake felt a huge gulf existed between him and his most recent students. He wondered if Shelby's generation was the last raised to tolerate quietness and stillness. It wasn't a judgment, just a reality. Perhaps such distraction is good, he'd thought at times after Melissa's death.

"We have a question for you," Shelby said, "about Uncle Walt during the war."

"I'll answer it if can," the old man responded. "But my memory's gotten near bad as my hearing and eyesight."

"Do you remember," Jake asked, "anything about a town called Cabrerets?"

"Don't know," the older man said. "We went through many a place, and lots of times we was too busy trying not to get shot to be looking for town signs."

"Yes, sir, I can imagine so," Jake said, taking out the map he'd printed off the internet. "I looked up the troop movements and it seems your division wasn't anywhere near there, but I wanted to be sure. The red mark I made, that's where the town was."

Mr. Winkler put his glasses back on, took the map, and placed it on his lap.

"Some of us come through there once, not during the war but right after."

"Right after?"

"Yeah, a few of us fellows had a three-day leave and took a train out of Paris. We was headed south toward Toulouse, but getting off the train when the notion took us. Anyways, at one stop, this Frenchman come on board jabbering about something interesting we might want to see, and said he'd drive us there and back."

"It was the cave, wasn't it?" Jake asked.

Winkler took off the glasses again and set them on the table. He looked at Shelby.

"So Walt told his brother about that?"

"About what, Mr. Winkler?" Shelby asked.

"Him being in that cave."

"That's what we want to know about," Jake said. "Were you in there with him?"

"Not the first time," the older man replied. "I wanted to flirt with them French girls instead of visiting some old cave, but Walt and a couple of fellows went to see it. The others caught back up with us and said it wasn't worth the time, that they'd seen better drawings in the funny papers. When we asked where Walt was they didn't know."

Winkler paused, and a smile creased his face, his eyes no longer focused on his visitors but something more inward.

"We figured he'd got one of them French girls to say *oui* to him."

"But it wasn't that?" Jake said.

"No, when it was near time to catch the next train, we started searching but it come to nothing until a Frenchman came and said Walt was in the way-back part of that cave, lying on the ground asleep. So me and another guy went in to get him. It was spooky in there, I tell you that, and got spookier the deeper we went. It had to be near a mile long. Darker than any place I've ever been, and what light we had showing these old-time fierce animals on the walls. When we finally found him he was lying on the cave floor fast asleep. We woke him up but he didn't want to leave. He said it was the first time he'd slept more than a couple of hours since coming ashore at Normandy. He started crying and saying that the only thing outside of that cave was death. We finally had to grab his arms and drag him out."

"So he was at the very back of the cave?" Jake asked.

"Yes, the very back. I didn't think we'd ever get him out of there," Mr. Winkler said. "But we did and took him to the train. The next week, Walt was headed home on a Section Eight. Some fellows in the unit thought bad of him for cracking up like that, but none of them was in that first wave at Omaha Beach. Walt was in the 116th Infantry. You know about them?"

"No, sir," Jake answered.

"Well, they was in the thickest of it. In his unit, Walt and two others came off that beach alive. Our outfit had some hard tussles, and Walt fought good as any man, but even then you could tell he was in a bad way."

"My daddy said Uncle Walt was never the same when he returned," Shelby said softly.

"None of us were, child," Winkler said, shaking his head. "It's just some could handle it better than others, or at least pretend to. My boys wanted me to go back over there a couple of years ago. They'd pay the flight, hotel, meals, everything. I told them thanks but that I'd spent most of my life trying to forget what I'd seen over there."

The old man shook his head even as he raised his hand and laid it on his brow. The nurse who'd been waiting beside the door came into the room.

"It's time for your lunch, Mr. Winkler."

Shelby nodded at the white box on the bureau.

"I baked you some gingerbread cookies. You can have them for dessert."

"Thank you, honey," he said, raising a trembling hand blotched purple-black. He held Shelby's hand a few moments before slowly releasing it. "Your uncle, he was a good man. We didn't do much talking, but if you've been through tough times together, you don't have to."

When Jake and Shelby got back to the farmhouse, Jake asked if he could see the paintings a last time.

"Sure," Shelby said, and lit the lantern.

They went into the house and down the dark hallway to the room. As their eyes adjusted, the menagerie slowly emerged. Shelby set the lantern down and stepped close to the lion. She placed her hands on the plywood and wiggled it until the two remaining nails pulled free. She carefully leaned the plywood against the wall.

"What will you do with it?" Jake asked.

"I don't know, but after what you told me on the way back about the other image, it wouldn't seem right not to save something. I might even put it up in the nursery. Matt will think it a strange notion but a pregnant woman has a right to a few of those."

Shelby leaned to pick up the lantern. When she stood again, the window's soft suffusing light surrounded her. *Woman With Lantern*, Jake thought. Perhaps somewhere such a painting existed. If not, he thought, it should.

"This may be the last time I see this room," Shelby said. "They're tearing it down next week. I wish the place wasn't being sold, but Daddy's giving Matt and me the money to build us a nice house on the far side of the ridge."

For a few minutes they were silent. Though it was mid-afternoon, the room was darkening. The animals began receding as if summoned elsewhere.

"I guess I'd better be getting home soon," Shelby said, "else Matt will start worrying."

Jake carried the plywood out and Shelby placed it and the lantern in the back of the jeep.

He opened the trunk of his car, then took out the sketch pads and boxes of crayons he'd bought at CVS.

"A gift for your son," he said. "Maybe he will be an artist like his great-great-uncle."

Shelby set the gifts beside the lantern and plywood.

"Thank you," she said, giving him an awkward hug, "not just for the gifts but for helping me find out about the paintings."

"I was glad to do it, Shelby," Jake said. "When your baby's born, I'd like to know."

"It won't be much longer," Shelby said, giving her stomach a soft pat. "The doctor says the third week in January."

"Cezanne was born around that date," Jake said. "The twentieth, I believe."

"Maybe I'll aim for that," Shelby said, smiling.

"Would you mind if I stayed a few more minutes?" Jake asked.

"No, sir," Shelby said, looking at the surrounding woods. "In the fall when the leaves turn, this cove is a real pretty place."

After Shelby left, Jake went back inside. He looked at the animals for a few minutes, then lay down on the moldering mattress. The springs creaked and a thin layer of dust rose and resettled. He closed his eyes. He did not realize that he had fallen asleep until he opened his eyes to total darkness. He felt his way through the house and out the door. In the day's last light, Jake drove slowly to the creek, stopped at the water's edge. Oak trees lined the opposite bank. In their upper branches, mistletoe clustered like bouquets offered to the emerging stars. He paused there a few more moments, then passed over.

ERIN SINGER

Spiders Come Quickly

Mornings while I brush my teeth I lay my four-month-old daughter on a towel on the floor of our glassed-in shower, safe and clean. The shower is tiled in button mushroom travertine and features a rainfall fixture and adjustable body sprays.

My baby's cry is a plaintive hollow sound in there. After I birthed her, the doctor prescribed peeing in the shower to lessen the sting. Natural remedies never help. To prevent ants from traveling up my bathroom vanity to eat my toothpaste, I tried sprinkling small piles of cinnamon where they crawl in through the baseboard. The next day, our cleaning lady mopped the cinnamon away. The ants remain.

The cleaning lady was my husband's idea. So was hiring a nanny. No doubt he would frown on my putting the baby in the shower, even for her protection. Secretly he thinks I am a bad mother even though I breastfeed exclusively. He was present when the lactation consultant told me to take off my nursing bra and, at the sight of my opal-veined boulder breasts, cried, Holy crap, those nipples look like raw hamburger meat!

And I said, Her mouth is a knife.

My husband tittered, What she means is—

The lactation consultant interrupted to dispatch him to Target for lanolin nipple cream.

Three weeks ago, I accidentally crushed an ant in the hinge that connects my toothpaste lid to the tube. The ant's body remains, a fleck of black pepper frozen in a gin-blue crust. If I were to die, perhaps my husband would ask one of the neighbor ladies to clean up my things (I have so few friends), and upon seeing the ant, the neighbor lady would understand that I was a disgusting person who hid behind a teeming blue recycling bin, a white SUV, large sunglasses, and reusable shopping bags from organic food markets. A truly decent person would've picked the ant out or not had a crust of toothpaste on the tube. Maybe not killed the ant at all.

Yesterday, my husband was poking around in my vanity, looking to borrow a few body wax strips for a pre-show de-furring, when he noticed all the ants around my sink. Call the exterminator, he said. We live in a desert, in a community called Kingsgate with armed guards and a clubhouse and two swimming pools and tennis courts. Andre Agassi is rumored to live here, as he is rumored to live in every upscale Las Vegas neighborhood because such rumblings are good for real estate.

Each morning, I walk my daughter in her stroller past the small pest control pickup trucks: BugRaiders, No Mercy, Pitbull. Without poison, ants multiply, stink bugs mate on our scalding driveway, rust-colored roaches scuttle away at the flick of the light switch, rats rush in from the golf course to nest in our eaves, spiders spin to feast on ants.

I told my husband that I expected the exterminator later this week, which was a lie. Memories had surfaced in my eighth month of pregnancy; I was crop dusted as a girl. My sister and I were playing on the dying lawn of our acreage as a plane buzzed low over the neighbor's wheat field. Light wind carried invisible flecks of pesticide to our cheeks. Traces of that pesticide are already lurking in my daughter's ovaries. In the eggs of my granddaughters. I canceled the exterminator that day.

My husband doesn't know about the dead ant in my toothpaste tube. He has his own pristine screw-top toothpaste, which is Arm & Hammer without whitening agents. He gets his teeth professionally whitened for free, which is one of the perks of being Las Vegas' premier hypnotist magician.

After I gave birth four months back, I tried Crest White Strips from the drugstore, figuring that if such a simple thing could improve my looks I should at least try. But those clear strips made my teeth gooey and sore. I stopped using them. Teeth aren't supposed to hurt. People always used to tell me what white teeth I had. This was the number one compliment I received from strangers. I credited my white teeth to nothing more than regular brushing.

No matter how tired I am I always brush my teeth twice a day, I bragged to my husband when we moved into our first apartment together and were still learning each other's habits. Scrunching his nose he said, Everyone brushes their teeth twice a day, don't they?

This comment made me think twice a day isn't enough. So now I brush my teeth three times a day, minimum, and still my mouth feels dirty. My whole body some days. Not long ago I was Las Vegas' premier hypnotist magician's assistant. Now, unless I am standing in the shower under a scalding rainfall, my body feels like an unbrushed tooth.

*

When I finish my morning grooming, my daughter and I retire to the living room where we relax on a flokati rug. One thing I always do is calculate breakfast points on my Weight Watchers app as my daughter sucks the fuzzy white strings out of the rug beneath us. Another thing I do is a Google image search of my name, my common married name, and every woman looks like a cleaned-up, LinkedIn-friendly version of me with beach waves and statement necklaces. A huge television plays constantly, though not any face I want to see. Where are you, Oprah? Imagine new motherhood with Oprah to rely on every day. But she's been lost to us for years now. Instead, a nineties sitcom-actress-turned-chef makes a chicken Caesar salad pizza and when she is done she takes one arm and sweeps the premade crust package and the salad dressing bottle into an off-camera garbage can.

Every Tuesday is recycling day at Kingsgate, though it's hard to tell on our morning walk. My desert companions despise recycling. Some of them pull two full trashcans to the curb on garbage day. I'm from a cold, flat Canadian town where only vulgar people don't recycle. Today, I push my daughter's stroller past house after house with no blue bin at the curb. Trash, I sing to her. Trash, trash, trash.

Our street is called Topgallant Royal Lane, "topgallant royal" being a sail on large ships. I had to look up the term. I know squat about boats. For centuries my ancestors have thrived in landlocked provinces, breeding offspring like cattle that can endure harsh winters, all to end up with me, a broad, tall, idle woman in a desert, staring out my kitchen window at the verdant green sea of the golf course beyond my backyard. My house is like all the other houses in Kingsgate, a style our realtor called "transitional" which is code for an absence of style: high ceilinged with textured spray drywall painted the color of sand, a kitchen like the inside of a Cheesecake Factory, home gym, California Closets, stone floors polished to a gleaming casino buffet shine, and that swimming pool. When my daughter and I walk Topgallant Royal Lane, the scenery behind us appears to be running on an endless loop like a Road-Runner cartoon. The air smells like fabric softener. The sidewalks are strewn with dead bees.

On this morning's walk, we stop to admire my neighbor's tree, which has a mound of gray root emerging from the ground like a dark brain.

The front door of the house opens and a tiny Yorkshire terrier trots out. If the dog sees us, she doesn't comment. The Yorkie squats on a patch of grass and pisses prissily. My neighbor calls this taking a tinkle.

Every month or so, Wanda's Washin' Wagon pulls up in front of this house. The van has a picture of a lap dog wearing an elegant purple sunhat. Last week, Wanda arrived at dusk as pink and golden orange washed the sky. It was still parked there an hour later when I dragged the garbage bin out to the curb in the new dark. The Washin' Wagon was lit from within. Wanda was alone inside, her gray hair raked back into a ponytail, a cigarette dangling from her thin lips as she swept dog hair from the grooming table to a dustpan. The desperation of a thousand Sunday afternoons settled in my bones.

Doggie, I say to my daughter, pointing to the peeing Yorkie on the lawn. Baby books warn to talk to your child incessantly or else she'll face certain doom—even when she is no more than a sweaty potato in a stroller. The landscape shifts in my periphery. Turning from the Yorkie, I see a coyote skulking through a cactus garden bordering the driveway. Its fur blends with the crushed rock.

Coyote, I whisper. Used to be I'd see coyotes running in the ditch alongside some prairie highway, always alone, not a friend for miles.

The Yorkie's tags jingle. Wanda had fixed tiny purple bows to its ears. I should've clapped my hands or made some sort of noise. Part of me was rooting for the coyote to take this dog in its teeth, clamp down on my neighbor's fur baby, carry it off into the desert and swallow it purple bows and all. I wanted my neighbors to get a taste of wildness, to know how cheap animals come in other parts of the world. No puppy Prozac. No massaged anal glands. No corn-free, refrigerated dog food. When my dog bit my baby cousin—almost tore his ear off—my uncle rushed him to the hospital and my dad loaded his rifle at our kitchen table. My sister ran upstairs to our bedroom and when the gun fired, I watched her fall to her knees and scream as if the bullet had torn through her heart.

The coyote watches the Yorkie circle a ratty stuffed duck toy. A desert breeze hot and dry as winter furnace air blows past my lips. Sweat trickles between my breasts. My daughter squalls, red and damp in her stroller seat. Alerting at the noise, the coyote darts among a row of fortnight lilies and disappears behind a casita. The door to the neighbor's house opens and a tuneless whistle carries out. The dog trots through, dragging the stuffed duck that is almost as big as she is.

Ants carry things thousands of times their body weight. The weight of a baby is almost nothing. Holding a child in one's arms, in one position, for hours upon hours, days upon days—that's what wears you down. Then again, I am not in good shape. Six weeks after I had the baby I purchased sessions with a personal trainer, firm of body and disposition. She escorted me to the leg press machine, moved the clip down way too far. I told her, There's no way I'm going to be able to press that much. And she said, You can press at least as much as you weigh. Realizing that she thought I weighed so much made me hate her; I quit the sessions. By then it was apparent that I would never be returning to the stage. One can't remain a magician's assistant forever. Who wants to see somebody's mom in a sparkly bikini top? Audiences need an ingénue, a girl they can fear for while she is being sawed in two. Should I die audiences would fear for my daughter, not me. The crowd would murmur, Not a very responsible mom, traipsing around getting sawed in half. If I die my husband will feel sad though. For whatever reason, he still loves me. He wants me to be happy. He tells me that every day. I just want you to be happy.

Who will replace me? I ask.

No one can replace you, he says.

There is a stack of headshots on his dressing-room table. In Las Vegas casinos rise and fall with the season. Everything is replaceable.

Target is walking distance from Kingsgate, but because of a) the heat and b) the gates surrounding the property that prevent me from taking the most direct route to the store, I drive. As we go to Target most weekdays, there isn't anything I need, though I put these items into the cart next to my baby's carrier: an indigo throw pillow, a bottle of blackest blue nail polish, a box of disposable diapers patterned with skulls and crossbones. The store is quiet, just me and the other suburban moms with babies, stretch pants, and roadkill eyes. If Oprah bumped into me on a Target run, she would assume I was part of this Target tribe. Oprah would look at me today and see a woman with a crooked ponytail and a tank top that says Brunch Lady clutching an empty Starbucks cup and pushing a cart full of landfill. I go back. I return every item to its original shelf, abandon the cart in the nail polish aisle and lug my daughter out the front doors, which part for me with a mechanical purr.

Inside the car the heat is like hands around my neck. My thighs burn against the leather seat. The steering wheel is so hot my driving gloves should be oven mitts. My husband is a responsible human. He covers his windshield with a screen so the car doesn't overheat and the interior upholstery doesn't fade.

In most ways, my husband is an excellent man. Our baby makes him happy. Most days he wakes up and goes to our daughter, raising her in the air like a sun offering and saying, I think we'll keep you. Meantime, I'm thinking, Let's go out for bagels and leave the baby at home.

When the doctor cleared the baby to travel at six weeks, we tried a beaching and birding vacation in Florida. Birds brought my husband to me, back when he was nobody. Nobody comes to my hometown. Lying in my bed the morning after his show, he told me he'd decided to tour through my dry province after reading about our wetlands in a birding magazine. I didn't know we had wetlands. He said, Come with me and see. I followed him through the marshes and around western Canada and across middle America until we alighted in Las Vegas, a city screaming with the dreams of puppeteers, drag queens, actors-turned-reality-stars-turned-Chippendale dancers, and Playboy bunnies put out to pasture.

I've never taken to birding—I prefer more sinister animals, ones lower to the ground. In Florida we visited the Everglades. I wore my daughter in a front-loading baby carrier. I slung my binoculars down my back and stepped off the walkway to observe an alligator in murk. The tops of my feet grew warm. They burned. Red ants frenzied over my feet and swarmed my legs, yet I couldn't bend over to brush them away. I cried out. I kicked off my ballet flats. My husband bent down and swatted at the fire ants. He crushed them. We both wound up with tiny red welts. Me on my feet and legs, him on his hands and arms. He didn't say I told you so, though he'd warned me about proper hiking shoes. Still, he could not deny the pain of his small wounds and he whined some. He is not used to moving about the world on fire.

That night, I took a cool bath in the shallow hotel tub. Underwater I am alone. I sink down and imagine I'm home, swimming in a green lake until my skull aches with cold. I imagine touching the sludgy lake bottom, transforming into a sinister northern mermaid with the translucent stalactite teeth of a walleye and slippery weeds for hair and a tail colonized by lashing black leeches. I will not sing for man. I will tip over fishing boats and bite dangling ankles.

In Las Vegas I have a swimming pool that overlooks the golf course. As a new bride, I used to lie out there on a floaty shaped like a pineapple and listen to the tock of balls as golfers teed off. The yard is too open, the water too clear, the sunshine too bright to feel alone underwater there. And besides, I can't go swimming anymore because if I go near the pool, I imagine myself throwing the baby in the water and watching her sink like a lead weight to the bottom. I don't actually think of throwing her in. I only see it happening. There is a safety gate around the pool now even though my baby can't walk. The gate is there to remind me.

For lunch most days I eat alone while my husband sleeps off his late work hours upstairs in a room darkened by blackout shades and cooled frigid with air conditioning. It is important for him to get his rest because he works and I don't. So I co-sleep with the baby in our master bedroom. While I make lunch, I strap the baby into a vibrating seat. Today, I drink a beer and cook a steak in a cast-iron skillet on my enormous gas range. Blue flames cup the bottom of the pan.

The steak is thick and salty. The beer is sharp and smells like fun. A bottle is three Weight Watchers points. I used to drink bottle after bottle until last call and then I'd walk across the parking lot to the convenience store and let whomever I was taking home that night buy me a fried chicken kebab.

When I met my husband, I was my most slender, my prettiest. There is a picture of us together, standing in front of the DJ booth the night we met. I'm wearing a pair of stretchy yoga pants and a fuchsia top because I came straight from work at Fitness Dynamics. My strange color in the photo is not due to bad lighting but to the daily minutes I logged in the tanning bed at the gym. It's all there in that photograph: the cheapness of my clothing, the way my bangs formed an egg-shaped crown atop my head, how my strange skin color made me look like an alien from an old Star Trek episode, a female alien still conventionally sexy enough to enchant Captain Kirk.

My husband caught me looking at the picture again yesterday.

I am fine, I told him. I have everything.

It's natural to feel bad sometimes, he said.

His opinion doesn't count, because he grew up rich. He grew up believing anyone can be anything, even something as ridiculous as a hypnotist magician.

Had I not, on a whim, abandoned my country to become the world's premier hypnotist magician groupie, probably I would be spritzing down a leg press at Fitness Dynamics right this minute. I would go over to the counter once in a while to check my phone and look at pictures of my baby in daycare and I would wish to have the exact life I have now: the pool, the husband, the baby, the palm trees, the sushi lunches, the whisper-quiet dishwasher into which I am now loading my bloody and pepper-speckled steak plate. A steak is twelve Weight Watchers points.

Before being placed on maternity leave, I split a dress onstage. As I bent to raise the lid of a magic trunk, the seams at my ass ripped. The wonderful acoustics of the casino theater amplified the noise, which was not unlike the accidental release of a desperately held-in fart. The audience roared. My husband rubbed his stomach and said, Avoid the hungry-man burrito at the twenty-four-hour café! Do I have permission to hypnotize all of you to forget I just did that? The audience roared again at his attempt to take the fall for me. I shuffled offstage sideways, showing the audience my teeth, which, from a distance, is almost the same as smiling.

Here's what I know: Never let anyone see you're splitting. Bury the Twinkie wrappers under the paper towels in the garbage. Mr. Clean the kitchen to oblivion. Wrap your soiled pads like toilet paper presents to the trashcan. Rub gardenia blossoms between your labia. Drive into desert night to defecate alone to the cry of coyotes. Swallow air.

I'm fine, I told my husband after my final show.

The baby won't go down for her nap this afternoon. Her cheeks are red, bottom gums enflamed. Her first tooth is about to break through. She cries a long jagged stream. I give her my knuckle and the hard little ridges of her gums work the bone. I love this almost-pain. I pace the house with her in my arms. I sit down on the couch and offer her my breast and she nurses until she goes slack. I'm afraid to move.

Over the phone, my mom, bread-baking breeder of six children, admonishes me to sleep when the baby sleeps. But I am American now. I choose what I do. So I turn on the TV to a marathon of *The Real Housewives of Beverly Hills* and *twitch jerk tickle* I'm asleep.

In a dream, my baby's teeth come in rotten, like the posters I'd see back home at the health clinic warning moms not to tuck their kids in with bottles of juice. And I dream of my daughter accusing me through a mouthful of snuff-spit brown teeth: This is because you played under the crop duster! This is because you drink beer at lunch! This is because you see me sinking in a pool!

I awake panicked because I've been seduced by the click-bait about engorged breasts smothering infants. The baby is still asleep, though some day she will talk to me. I rewind *Housewives*. Lately I watch so much television I don't bother with contacts. The dry air makes the lenses thick in my eyes. The girl I was would be aghast at the thought of wearing glasses in front of her husband. Back then I was eager to please. At the bar, I did things with my mouth—tie cherry stems, lick the dribbling foam from pints, suck chicken wing sauce off the length of my fingers—to make men picture me sucking their dicks. What I didn't think about was the women who were present, watching a persimmon-skinned girl tonguing a Jell-O shot for the benefit of some douchebag and thinking, *Grow a brain you whore.*

I have new glasses that make me look smarter. When I wear them I feel like me from a parallel life. The frames are very large, meant for a trendy girl working a department store makeup counter or a stylish attorney in a courtroom drama. I picked them out when the baby was one month old. I went to the ophthalmologist about a floater in my right eye. Supposedly, she is the best ophthalmologist in Las Vegas. The walls of her waiting room were filled with framed photographs of her dressed in evening gowns standing next to celebrities such as Usher and Carrot Top. She checked my eye and said, Yes, you have a floater.

Apparently, it's common for women to get floaters after giving birth, along with fire bladders and hamburger nipples and shedding and collapsing vaginas and ballooning hemorrhoids and capillaries bursting like fireworks. Breathing deeply, I nodded and said, OK, let's get to the bottom of this. And she said, You're at the bottom. You have a floater.

As I watch *Housewives,* I spot a new floater in the other eye. A black squiggle worms over my vision. So I close an eye and focus and see a tiny ant traipsing over the lens of the glasses, which rest on my bathroom vanity at night. Fury zaps my body. Rage at the ant for making me worry about having a second floater, for stealing my enjoyment of my daughter's nap. I squish him. The motion startles my baby awake. She cries. Leaving her on a teething toy–strewn blanket on the flokati rug,

I stomp to the bathroom with a full bottle of Evian water. I rinse all the ants scurrying about my sink down the drain. I yell at them, Tell your friends!

The hollering wakes my husband. He carries my baby into the bathroom, looking tired. The empty water bottle crackles in my hand. I tell him, You might think I'm crying but no. I have something in my eye. An ant has crawled from my glasses and was crumpled to death by my eyelid.

And he says, You're pale.

I take her for a walk every day. Outside. Every single day.

Why don't we go out in the backyard, babe, he yawns. Let's go lie in the sun.

It's not safe back there.

What do you mean?

He closes in on me. The baby's mouth breaks into a wide grin at my face. From her bottom gum a small sliver of tooth has emerged, the color of milk in my body.

The joy in her eyes moves to my heart as the golf ball flies over the fence and strikes her perfect soft skull. As she slips from my hands into the pool. As the coyote carries her little body off through the flash flood channel and into the desert. As the spiders hurry up her legs and bite.

My husband doesn't see all this. He can't understand: First come the ants. Then come the spiders.

Before I cooked my steak on the stove at lunch, I went in the backyard to turn on the barbecue. As I loosened the propane tank valve, a black widow crawled up my fingers. My hand jerked away. Biology controlling my body. How I hate myself for not holding on. For not letting the black widow sink its fangs into my flesh and filling me with venom. That would be an emergency. That would be reason to tell my husband, I am dying.

SERENE TALEB-AGHA
A Hiker's Guide to Damascus

Syria is the country where I first began to hike. I had moved there from the US with my husband in the early 2000s to the approving nods of the elders of my family. Before then, I'd only gone on visits, to see relatives and learn the language. My move was supposed to be a homecoming. A graft cut from a tree only thrives in its native soil, my relatives told me. Syria is the only country where you will be unconditionally embraced. In the ambivalent years following 9/11, when I began to be noticed as something more than an oddly dressed woman whose parents came from a country no one had ever heard of, it sounded like an easy route to acceptance.

It turned out the acceptance was not so unconditional—more on that later—but it also turned out there was much more to embrace than the people. To this day, when I think of Damascus, I think of the land that cradles it: the pockmarked hills with sharp spines down their ridges like the bones of a stegosaurus, where the rains have etched away at the limestone; the dry valleys, where the road is rough, the water scarce, and you wouldn't venture without a friend. In other words: hiking country.

I had trouble making friends the first couple of years. Then my husband read an article in an online paper about a hiking club and, knowing that I had a love for nature, forwarded it to me. That was how I found myself at a bus depot in downtown Damascus very early one weekend, prepared to take a bus ride off into the countryside with a few dozen complete strangers.

They called themselves the Nature Explorers, and unlike the independent, go-it-alone streak of the American hikers I've hiked with since, they considered themselves a family. Everyone paid a small fee, which went to the purchase of common meals, and before we embarked on the bus, we divided the packets of olives and cheese for breakfast, beans or pasta for lunch, into our packs. The bus was barely big enough to fit half of us, and most of the young men stood in the aisle. Leaving the city, the driver would play the mellow strains of Fairouz, the Lebanese diva. On the way home, our feet sore from ten to fifteen miles of all-day traveling, those still left with energy cranked up the dance music and clapped and shook their hips in the aisles.

Hiking is not a commonly recognized sport in Syria, and most of the time, especially in the drier areas, there wasn't even a trail. As for the Ghouta, the flood plain to the south of the city, the land was almost all carved up into privately owned orchards. There seemed to be an unstated rule that passing through was allowed so long as we picked no fruit and broke no branches, but sometimes the landowner would send a family member to keep his eye on us and get us moving if we stayed too long. The club, I was told, had been started by a Frenchman, but all he had done was organize something that was already familiar to many of them. One of my fellow hikers, Raida, had grown up playing in the hills around the middle Syrian town of Safita. The slopes and valleys had been her playground, and she was so quick at jumping and hopping over rocks that I was afraid I would trip if I tried too hard to keep up. These hikes were her only chance to breathe in the fresh air of her childhood. Now she lived in a tiny apartment in the city. "All I want is a balcony to sit on and enjoy the cool evenings," she said. "Just a balcony!"

On my first hike with the Nature Explorers, I hadn't yet met Raida, or any of the other friends that would reveal to me the fascinating diversity that was the people of Damascus. I spent half the day climbing the gritty brown hills to the north of the city, frequently slipping until a woman told me I'd have better footing if I stepped on the low scrubby plants that dotted the hills. As if in initiation, the club leader insisted I take a turn carrying the cauldron that we used to cook lunch. By the time we stopped to rest, in a small olive orchard in a fold of hill, my thighs were burning. The others spread out their picnic blankets and gathered into groups. I'd forgotten to bring one, and shyly sat underneath a tree, alone. "Hey," called a man from under the next tree. "We don't allow people to sit alone here," he said, laughing, and invited me to join his friends on the blanket.

When I tell American friends about my Syrian hiking club, they're surprised. They don't imagine Syrians as free spirits, trekking the wilderness. It doesn't fit the usual Arab stereotypes of, I don't know, reading the Qur'an in a dark corner of a mosque, or spending all day in the kitchen stuffing grape leaves. Of course, this was before the war, before the only thing that people associated with Syria was pain and ruin. But my Syrian family members were equally surprised. They are Sunni Muslims from Damascus, and hopeless city slickers. They love watching sunsets and hillscapes—if it's from a covered restaurant terrace. They will picnic along the riverside if the orchard owner has tables and chairs for rent and a boy to bring them hot tea. Like city slickers the world over—they don't *do* dirt. Or bugs.

As a Damascene Sunni, I stood out a bit among the Nature Explorers. Most of them were migrants of some kind, or the children of migrants. The vast majority came from the Syrian countryside, looking for a better life in the city, and were a medley of religions and sects: Sunni Muslim, Christian, Alawite, Druze. We had Palestinian descendants from the refugee crises of the wars with Israel in 1948 and 1967, as well as recent arrivals fleeing unrest in Iraq. There was a young Iraqi man who always brought his guitar, and, in one surreal moment, he pulled it out at a lunch stop and sang a faithful rendition of "Country Road" against the backdrop of the Syrian wilderness.

Like my fellow hikers, I was also a migrant in a sense, having grown up in the US, a child of Syrian immigrants, then moving to Syria as an adult. Before that continent-wide move, I'd participated in the great American tradition of moving from city to city to follow opportunity, crisscrossing the US from one coast to the next. I learned not to let my roots grow too tight into the ground. I learned to have random conversations with people in restaurant lines or at train stops because who knows if you'll ever meet them again? The Nature Explorers were something I, as an American, knew—people who were willing to talk with you for as long as you happened to be walking beside them on the trail.

Outside of hiking, I mixed with Sunni Damascene society, where the rules were very different. Here, I had two social circles. The first was extended family. We shared dinner with my husband's parents, siblings, and nieces and nephews every single Friday without fail, crowded around my mother-in-law's large dining room table or, when she got tired of cooking, on long restaurant tables, three or four of them lined end to end. We also frequently visited uncles, aunts, and cousins on Thursday nights. The second social circle was my neighbors.

These gatherings were frequently structured around religious activities and, unlike the hiking club, were women-only. We met in parlors, sitting in fancy carved chairs that lined the walls, the heavy drapes closed so gardeners or caretakers wouldn't peer in. Sometimes we invited a speaker from a popular women's religious organization to give a talk. If a neighbor had lost a relative, we would meet to recite the Qur'an over the deceased's soul. The host would place the thirty slim volumes on a marble-topped table and we divided them among ourselves until every single word was read. We went to each other's houses to celebrate marriages, births, a daughter putting on the hijab for the first time. One childless neighbor liked to bring us together for extravagant brunches featuring at least a dozen dishes, all cooked from scratch in her own kitchen.

In the parlors of my neighbors' houses, there were no strangers. Everybody knew who you were, where you came from. When I was introduced to someone for the first time, I was presented as "Serene, from the Taleb-Agha family." They might remind the listener what my family was known for, textile manufacturing in the Old City, and also mention my husband's family name. In this way, I, and every other person in the group, was precisely located in the dense web of Damascene interfamilial relationships. All of us were from Damascene families, or families that had migrated to Damascus sufficiently long ago to count.

I've never been a chameleon. I was the same person on the trail as I was sipping Turkish coffee in a fancy parlor. The Nature Explorers, for the most part, were a secular crowd. I was one of the few who wore hijab. No one else, as far as I could tell, tried to squeeze in their prayers during rest stops as I did, making my ablutions out of a plastic water bottle and spreading my jacket on the ground as a makeshift prayer rug. I did not judge. I accepted my fellow hikers as they were; I expected them to do the same for me. On one hike, I drew aside during our lunch stop to pray the noon prayer. One of my hiking companions told me afterward how she wished she had grown up with rituals like mine, with prayers that divided up the days, and fasts that slowed you down in your rush of living. She craved the cadence, the structure of religious ritual, something her Druze religion, with its emphasis on individual spiritual discovery, did not provide. "But," she said, "your people don't like to mix much with others, isn't that true?" And I had to admit she was right. Damascene Muslims liked their traditions, and didn't like having to bend them to accommodate other religions.

It's hard to imagine how my hiking friends and my neighbors could have come together. The same online article that had introduced me to the club had also incited a comment war between club members and those who faulted them for skipping Friday congregational prayers in order to hike. The speaker my neighbor friends invited to their houses frequently cautioned us against social activities in which men and women mixed together. Even a married couple sharing dinner with family friends was dangerous. "How many women have introduced their husbands to their friends" she said, "and then beaten themselves up with regret after the devil put evil thoughts in his head!" My neighbors may not all have followed her advice strictly, but the idea of men and women sitting on a picnic blanket together, drinking from the same cup of *mate* that they passed around the circle, would have thrown them into fits. They shared the same country, but the cultural divide was too great.

It seemed like the Nature Explorers were trying, at least, to bring people together. The club leaders bragged about the diversity of their people. I personally experienced generous acts of sectarian acceptance. On only my second hike, I slid down a steep bank to make my ablutions in a creek. While struggling to climb back up, I was given a friendly hand by Majid who, in his late sixties, was our oldest hiker and also a Christian. And there was one of our most memorable hikes, an off-road trek to the mountaintop monastery of Deir Mar Musa, made famous by the Italian priest Father Paolo, who helped restore it and turn it into a spiritual retreat for people of all faiths. Father Paolo would later disappear during the war while trying to reconcile warring factions in north Syria, and many fear he is dead. On that day, he was full of life, busy tending to the crowd of weekend visitors, but he generously lent us the use of the monastery kitchen so that we could prepare our lunch. Later, it was time for my own prayers, but I hesitated doing so at a Christian place of worship. I asked my Alawite friend, Katya, if she thought anybody would take offense. She told me to go ahead. "God," she replied, "is everywhere."

I hiked on and off with the Nature Explorers for four years. My last hike with them was in late February of 2011. I planned to join them for their next hike two weeks later, but before that happened, protests erupted in Daraa province. The club cancelled the hike and immediately suspended all its activities. I stayed in Syria for another year and a half while I watched the country around me grow increasingly militarized. When it became clear the war wasn't going to go away, I took my children and moved back to America, the country of my birth.

We eventually settled in Georgia, in an Atlanta suburb. Unlike some of our family and friends, I was lucky to leave before actually witnessing any violence. But the anxiety of war was hard to shake off. Whenever I saw a person in camo—a common sight in Georgia—I cringed. I remember taking the kids to a war-themed laser tag hall and laughing at the sound recording of shelling. It sounded tinny and false, but also reminded me of the real thing. The memories faded with time, and as I struggled to acclimate my children to the new school system, other, older memories came back: days as a public-school student, the only Arab kid in a classroom of white and Asian students; days as a young mother on my very first short hikes at local parks in the Seattle suburbs, hoisting my baby son to my back when he got tired so I could keep going longer. I volunteered at my children's school, got a job, and of course hiked, for miles at a time, often alone or with only a single other companion, another mother from my children's school. It seemed as though everything had changed. I was so enmeshed in my new life that I couldn't imagine going back to Syria. I hardly even remembered it.

Then came Donald Trump's election to the presidency, and the anger and vitriol that accompanied the long campaign season. And I couldn't help it. It's happening again, I told myself. This is how wars start. And just when I convinced myself I was being paranoid, I'd remember how barely a year before the March protests, everyone thought Syria was on the cusp of economic prosperity. No one imagined a war—not so soon.

We are barely months into Trump's presidency and already much of his and his supporters' anger is directed at people like me. The outsiders, the immigrants, the ones who left the familiarity, and the poverty, of their home towns for a better chance here. These are exactly the kinds of people I hiked with in Syria, the ones that established Damascene families looked down on. Being on the inside, I knew. I heard the comments firsthand from my own people. There was Um Hani, an older friend who hosted a Muslim parenting discussion group in her home. She was a gem of a woman. Where other Damascene families spent thousands of pounds on crystal chandeliers and fancy Oriental rugs to show off their wealth, she kept a simple living room with a jar on the table for charity. "Anyone who's late," she growled, with a twinkle in her eye, "pays a mandatory donation!" But even she was uncomfortable with all these migrants from the countryside and their strange ways. "Damascus was a beautiful city," she said. "Then all these outsiders came and ruined it." I heard the same sentiment repeated by many of my older relatives. In ways, it was understandable. Over their lifetimes, they had watched Damascus balloon from a well-contained city of half a million to a sprawling and overcrowded metropolis fifteen times as big. They were used to a society where everyone obeyed the rules, even if they didn't believe in them. Damascene Christians in past generations, they told me, used to refrain from eating in public during Ramadan out of deference to Muslim sensibilities. Christians read the Qur'an at school, enjoyed its poetry, studied it for its grammar, even if they didn't believe in its divine origin. Then the masses had moved in from the countryside, many of whom called themselves Muslim but looked blankly at you when you quoted a verse of the Qur'an to them, people who ate and drank publicly during Ramadan, and who slept through the Friday congregational prayer. What was worse—these same outsiders had taken over the government and essentially shut out the Damascene families from power for the past fifty years.

The government was controlled by only a handful of Alawite families, which meant that the vast majority of newcomers to Damascus were equally excluded from the political process. But when people are resentful, they draw large, sloppy X marks. It's easier to just hate everybody who is not like you. I used to live in a suburb of Damascus that was an unusual mix of Sunni Muslim, Christian, and Alawite. When the man I bought fish from found out where I lived, he told me he had visited my town once on a summer evening and watched with horror as the Alawite families strolled through the streets in their tracksuits, men and women together, the women enjoying the cool evening breezes blowing through their loose hair. "When I saw that sight, I got out," he said. "I wouldn't live there if you paid me!" It's easy enough to call him a bigot, to shake our heads as Americans at the close-mindedness of other cultures—but the racial segregation of our own neighborhoods proves the hateful things we whisper when we are with our own.

In Syria, I saw the mistrust from the Muslim side, but I have no doubt the same sentiments were mirrored in all the sectarian communities of the country. My son made a few Christian friends at school. I thought it would be easy to make friends with their mothers. I had grown up in a largely Christian country. I knew what being a religious minority was like. But at their birthday parties, I would walk up to the circle of mothers and be greeted with a sudden silence. Even when one of them seemed friendly, she'd speak awkwardly, carefully, as if afraid she might cause offense. And then there was the year my daughter decided she wanted to wear the hijab. One of the Christian mothers never gave up an opportunity to take me aside and tell me I was being cruel by forcing my daughter to cover her hair. It didn't matter how many times I told her that it had been completely my daughter's decision, that I had even told her to think about it carefully before she committed. The mother refused to believe it. "To you your religion, and to me mine," the Qur'an says, but it seemed like Syrian culture never fully embraced it.

The Nature Explorers had only partly been able to break these sectarian walls down. They had brought the minorities together, the outsiders, but they were barely able to make a crack against Damascene Sunni society. And that was before the war. Once the war started, more fissures appeared. Katya, my Alawite friend, and Manal, a mostly secular Sunni from Daraa, stopped speaking to each other after a fierce political argument. Each, in her fear, had run for shelter to her own tribe. It was as though the long conversations on the picnic blanket had never happened, like we'd never held out our hands to steady each other while sliding down slopes, slippery with dust.

Those old hikes seem a universe away. Katya and I exchange the occasional Facebook message, but other than that, the Nature Explorers are completely gone from my life. The Syrian war grinds on, not wanting to finish. Friends ask me how it is over there, frowning in comfortable concern. We complain to each other about Trump and his over-the-top pronouncements, on how the illegals are bringing drugs and crime into this country, how refugees are clawing in, eager for their first opportunity to inflict terror attacks. They will bring *sharia* instead of democracy. They will force our women into harems. Yes, the hordes are coming in, eager to destroy our heritage, replace it with theirs. I have heard this before.

As a Muslim American, as a woman of Syrian ancestry in the United States, I am one of these outsiders. But I've also seen what it's like to be on the inside. Change is frightening. We spend years as children learning what's right behavior: shake hands, look each other in the eye, mow your lawn up to your property line, don't let your children run through the grocery store aisles. All these little habits that keep society going. Then new people move in, people who don't know the rules. It would be one thing if they weren't so many. Then you could patiently put up with them until they learned. But when they come in by the thousands, when so many of their children flood the school that your children start picking up their habits—yes, I understand how people can freak out. They want to press rewind, want things to go back to the way they used to be. Somebody changed the rules on them while they weren't paying attention. It's not fair.

But when did we get promised that the world wouldn't change? The newcomers aren't going to pack up and go home because you don't like them. They're here. Just like the Palestinians and the Iraqis and the Alawites and the Druze who came to Damascus. They weren't going home. Home might be dangerous, if you were Iraqi, or off-limits, if you were Palestinian, or even if it was a safe village in the countryside— how many pounds a year can you make tilling a small plot of land on a mountainside? Should you be condemned to live forever on the piece of geography where you were born?

One hiker named Aseel drove this point home for me. As we sat on a bare, rocky plain one hot summer afternoon, waiting for the sun to lose its edge before we started hiking again, she told me her story. She was a Palestinian refugee. "But I'm actually originally Moroccan," she said. Her ancestors had moved to the Holy Land in the early twentieth century. They happened to be living there when the British occupiers created the state of Israel in 1948. They hung on until the 1967 war, when they fled to Syria. "It's the way of all people to migrate for a better life," she said. "But we were in the wrong place at the wrong time, and now we're stuck forever being Palestinian." Israel would not grant her citizenship; neither would Syria. The papers linking her to Morocco were lost long ago. She was stateless, unable to travel, living off of the meager consolation of UN grant money and her family's own hard work. This is the way the modern world treats those who dare travel far from their birthplace—even if your birthplace is nothing like what it was when you were born there.

We are all going to lose our homelands. Either we will have to leave them, or we'll have to watch as strangers come into them. It is the way of the world. Like the old Damascene families, the (mostly European white) American privileged classes are fighting it, though in some states, they have already lost their majority. And if Syria is an example—it could end badly.

Shortly after Trump's inauguration, a few members of a local women's group swung by my mosque to drop off a box of doughnuts. They had written messages all over the box. "We stand united with our Muslim brothers and sisters," they said. "America for all!" During the week of the immigration ban, friendly demonstrators stood in front of the mosque during Friday prayers, holding up signs of support. These are people we share coffee with, invite into our mosque for interfaith gatherings. These are our Nature Explorers. We share a picnic blanket. But will it be enough?

My most difficult hike in Syria gives a hint of an answer. I had traveled with the Nature Explorers to an expanse of lava called the Lajat located southeast of Damascus. The Lajat is fifteen miles wide, and completely uninhabited except for the occasional shepherd pasturing his sheep on the sparse seasonal pasture. The land undulated in waves beneath our feet, as if it had been caught by surprise while still liquid. As it froze, it had shrunk and cracked, the black sheets of lava crumbling underneath their weight into deep depressions. We clambered down large boulders only to clamber back up again, over and over.

It was an eerie and beautiful land, black everywhere except for the lichen that speckled the rock in patches of ghostly white or rich golden yellow. Katya and I helped each other across the deep crevices. Sunset approached, but still, the sunken rocks stretched all the way to the horizon. We never hiked after dark. I imagined we would abruptly reach the end, that it would take us by surprise the way trails sometimes did. The sun's disk slipped away and no word was said. We hiked on, and as the sky darkened, we saw the light from a single minaret wink in the distance.

I hadn't brought a flashlight. I pressed my cell phone buttons to turn on the screen and cast a little extra light over the rocks I was climbing. Whenever the minaret looked close, we'd descend into a depression and it would disappear. We would struggle out and see the minaret again, only a little closer. Again, it would disappear, then reappear again. It was like a torture someone had invented.

I tripped and my phone clattered over a boulder. I grabbed it before it disappeared into a crevice and prayed I wouldn't twist an ankle, that I wouldn't be left in the dark, alone, in the cold, with absolutely no way to navigate. My phone battery was getting low. I shut the lid down on my bubbling panic. At one point, a woman asked me if I was crying.

"I *want* to cry," I replied.

She was one of those loud-mouthed women who can't mind their own business. She announced to the entire group that I needed help. I hated her. But I also could not handle seeing that minaret disappear on me one more time. A young man wearing a headlamp slipped out of the crowd, and took my hand without saying a single word. He didn't embarrass me by asking my name or whether I was OK. But his headlamp cast a joyous circle of light ahead, outlining the rocks and crevices. He led me out, all the way to the mosque on the edge of the Lajat, as if I were a little child being led out of danger by an older brother.

The bus was waiting for us next to the mosque and we all made it home safely. But for weeks afterward, I was gripped by the shame and fear of those couple of hours. I had realized how fragile I was in a way that years of comfort had made me completely forget. I had wandered close to something that looked like death.

It seems funny now to have panicked about something so small. A sprained ankle, a cold night out in the open, was the worst that could have happened. It's like I needed to literally feel the rocks, hard and rough beneath my hands and feet, in order to wake the fear. But if there's a time to panic, it should be now. There's the war I left in Syria, the one that has already consumed lives in the hundreds of thousands. And there is the war—if we can call it that—brewing right before our eyes on American soil. Protesters clash in the streets a little more frequently than is comfortable. Citizens in my home state of California talk of secession and for once, it's not a total joke. Commentators tell us that our nation is being torn apart, but it's likely that even they can't imagine what that means exactly. We may yet make it across this rugged and desolate land, but is any of us completely sure?

Katya knew more than I did what it took to make it across intact. I called her after the Lajat hike because I had no one else to talk to. The rest of my family never strayed far from three square meals and a comfortable chair in a well-lit parlor. They wouldn't understand. I asked her if she panicked, if she thought she wouldn't make it across, or feared for her sixty-year-old mother whom she'd brought along.

"Serene, why were you so scared?" she asked me. "We were together."

And maybe in the face of an unimaginable danger, that is the only answer. Helping each other down the boulders. Holding each other's hands, despite differences in background or political disagreements. Sharing a picnic blanket, sipping from the same cup of *mate*. Together.

SU TONG
Arrowhead Tubers

Translated from the Chinese by Ting Wang

Upon returning home, the first things my auntie saw were two big speckled roosters encircled by net bags. One squatting, the other standing, both appeared fairly sagacious. Once she spotted the roosters, Auntie knew my cousin was back. She looked carefully at the ground—maybe the roosters had good hygiene or they were too empty-stomached to foul it; anyhow, it was rather clean. Auntie grabbed one rooster's crest, examined it. "They'd better not be infected," she muttered. "It's always rooster, rooster; couldn't he bring something else? They don't make good stewed soup, nor do they lay eggs; plus, they're deadly noisy in the morning." Auntie walked to the kitchen's entrance. She was just about to get some rice to feed the roosters when she caught sight of a stranger—a young lady wearing a fuchsia shirt— sitting on the patio and rubbing arrowhead tubers with a small piece of unglazed porcelain.

Thinking that my cousin had brought back his girlfriend, Auntie became a little excited but also a bit nervous. She sneaked into the kitchen like a thief and then came out. Smoothing over her hair with one hand, she stood there and started fake coughing. The young lady rubbing the arrowhead tubers raised her head, revealing a dusky but rosy face, which betrayed her as a girl from the countryside. She sprang from her stool, trying to force herself to smile at Auntie, out of either shyness or politeness. Auntie heard her utter, indistinctly, a salutation in a rural dialect that was hard to make out and puckered her eyebrows subconsciously. The young lady let her hands droop; her eyes bounced onto Auntie for a bit but were quickly withdrawn. She looked timidly toward my cousin's room and suddenly called out, "Comrade Yang, please come out, come over here." The moment my bleary-eyed cousin walked out, she ducked into the room, her head hanging down. Seeing Auntie quite taken aback, my cousin rubbed his stomach and smiled dryly, "Why are you goggle-eyed? Thought I brought back my girl-friend? I am not so progressive as to get myself a girlfriend from the countryside!" Auntie waited for him to explain further, but he merely pointed toward the guest inside his room and the two roosters on the ground. "That's Gu Caixiu from Gu Village," he said cursorily. "She got into hot water and needs to stay here for a couple of days—just to lay low until the storm passes."

However convoluted Caixiu's story was, it should have unfolded within the confines of Auntie's home, with no entanglement whatso-ever with my family. But that night, Auntie, carrying one basket of arrowhead tubers and with burning anxiety, scurried to my home. She said she had an urgent matter to discuss with my mom. It actually was about Caixiu, not a case of real urgency. But the tone Auntie used to describe it made it sound like a life-and-death situation and bespoke its thorniness. I was fairly young then and knew nothing about exchange marriage—the form of marriage prevalent in the countryside. I was only able to make out the exchange relationship involved, which was very much like the equation we learned in math class: $X+Y=X1+Y1$. Caixiu's elder brother got himself a wife, so his wife's elder brother, in turn, would get Caixiu as his wife. Auntie made a point of mentioning that the man was a lot older, had epilepsy, and bit off his own tongue during one outbreak—so among other things, he was tongueless. At this point, Mom couldn't help crying out loud, "No way! To marry a normal, fine girl to a fella with no tongue? Isn't Chairman Mao pre-siding over Gu Village? They don't treat female comrades like human beings. Her parents did such a brainless thing, and the Party isn't even lifting a finger?"

"Knock it off," said Auntie. "The village's Party branch is busy learn-ing from Dazhai.[1] They are so swamped that they couldn't care less about whose families are arranging exchange marriage.

---

1. Here "Dazhai" refers to the "Learn from Dazhai in Agriculture" cam-paign that was launched and carried out in the 1960s, which encouraged peasants from all over China to follow the example of the farmers in Dazhai Village in Shanxi Province, who were claimed to have increased harvests through self-sacrifice and devotion to Maoist political goals. It was intended to uphold the spirit of self-reliance, hard work, and collec-tivism, and to increase agricultural production and efficiency.

The trouble," she continued, "is that it's a done deal—Caixiu's elder brother has already married the fella's younger sister, but now Caixiu isn't willing to be married off to the other family after receiving ideological guidance from some educated urban youth."

Auntie mentioned an educated young woman named Gong Aihua. She said Caixiu had intended to sacrifice herself for her brother, but it was Gong Aihua who opposed it, made the decision on her behalf, and even laid out a detailed escape plan for her. Auntie accused Caixiu's parents of being cruel and unscrupulous and throwing their daughter under the bus for the sake of their son. But on the other hand, she kept on blaming Gong Aihua. "She's a showboat, a careerist! She went down to the countryside despite advice against it, just to get coverage in the newspaper!" she said. "Once there, she's still getting ahead of everyone else, again to get publicity in the paper, and she's using Caixiu as a mere stepping stone." With some resentment in her voice, Auntie continued, "I'm not against her outdoing others, nor against her saving someone's bacon. But she can't just take all the credit while throwing the dirty work upon others. My son, Big Kitten, is a complete airhead. He likes to be bossed around by Gong Aihua—he brought Caixiu back home as he was told. Our home is so crammed already, and I've got boys only—am I supposed to host a country girl there as an overnight guest? That will get all the gossip going!" By this point, Auntie realized that Mom hadn't expressed anything after accepting the arrowhead tubers, so at long last, she divulged the matter of urgency. "We've got no space at home to set up a bed for her. My niece sleeps in the attic by herself. How about having that girl stay in the attic with my niece? For five days, five days only. You would be doing me a favor." Auntie stretched out one hand, palm outwards, and kept waving it in front of Mom's face until she nodded her head. Finally, Auntie breathed a sigh of relief. "My airhead son said my home is the first transit station, and there will be other liaison stations and command posts—they are pursuing this as a grand revolutionary cause!" she said. "Once Gong Aihua is back for the National Day holiday, I will have Big Kitten send that girl to her home. As I told Big Kitten, with all the kids, our home has got heavy enough traffic, and isn't fit for a transit station for others!"

I knew nothing about that country girl called Caixiu, but I did know about the Gong Aihua that Auntie mentioned. She was a different breed of educated youth from my cousin—she was hailed as a role model by the authorities. Her photo was featured on my school's bulletin board displays—a girl with big eyes, an oval face, wearing a large red flower pinned to her chest. Since her body was turned at a slight angle, with a faraway, and upward—yes, upward—look in her eyes, that pose, to me, encapsulated her communist aspirations.

Later that night, my cousin, holding a flashlight, sent Caixiu and a rooster to my home. As if he were sending two pieces of luggage under guard, once they were dropped in the warehouse, he just turned tail and ran off. Mom asked him to take back home the basket that had contained the arrowhead tubers; he agreed to that but still left it in the corner behind the door.

Just like that, Caixiu became the guest of my family.

The rooster was put under an inverted wooden crate on the patio. Caixiu and my elder sister were sharing the attic. My family had never hosted such a guest; she was not a relative, but the same courtesy was extended to her as we would to relatives. The first morning, Mom made her a bowl of poached eggs. After some demur, and having no clue how to show appreciation, she took the bowl and ate one egg. Suddenly, she caught sight of the look in my eyes, and instantly she found a way to show gratitude. She pushed the bowl toward me. "Let the little brother have them," she said. "We've got plenty of eggs in the countryside. I eat them pretty often." Mom was deterring me verbally, yet her eyes expressed appreciation for Caixiu; I could see that, so I took the bowl of eggs outside to eat. Mom didn't try to stop me again. "Have some congee then," she said casually to Caixiu. "Having congee in the morning is most soothing on the stomach—it's easy to digest."

I caught a glimpse of the way Caixiu ate her congee. She stuck her whole face into the bowl; foregoing the chopsticks and holding the bowl in both hands, she was pouring the congee into her mouth— almost as if she was drinking water.

"Slow down, Caixiu, there's a big pot of it," Mom said. "Caixiu, did you sleep well last night?"

She didn't know how to give a perfunctory response like the city people. She thought for a bit and shook her head. "I woke up several times," she said. "How come there were train and steamboat whistles at night? They scared me."

"I thought you slept well—you didn't get up until eight o'clock! I heard you snore." Looking askance at Caixiu, my sister grumbled, "I was the one who didn't sleep well. I woke up at six o'clock, woken by your teeth grinding!"

"Your ears are too delicate; just some teeth grinding was enough to wake you up?" Mom interrupted my sister. "Folks in the countryside are used to drinking unboiled water, have roundworms in their tummies, and they all grind their teeth at night." She then asked, "Caixiu, do you get up at eight o'clock at your home too?"

"The rooster didn't crow. I thought it wasn't daybreak yet. Back in our village I wake up to the crows of roosters. It's odd that here the trains and steamboats whistle at night, whereas the rooster doesn't crow." Casting a glance at the patio, Caixiu murmured, "The rooster also seems shy around strangers and stops crowing in the city."

"The rooster is gone," said Mom. "The kids' dad killed it early this morning. It will be marinated and made salted chicken for the Spring Festival."

The kitchen fell silent. Caixiu put down her congee bowl, looking astounded for some unknown reason. Her facial expression made us all inexplicably uncomfortable. My sister's shrill voice rose, "Ours is a model street of good hygiene. Raising chickens is forbidden!"

Caixiu walked aslant toward the patio; her face turned a bit gray. Leaning against the doorframe, she glanced at the naked rooster hung on the clothes line and said nothing. But I could tell she was very upset.

"Raising chickens is not allowed here." Mom followed her over. She comforted Caixiu while surveying her face: "It was just a rooster, not a rabbit or a lamb. Why is it so hard for you to part with it? Chickens are to be killed once they are full grown."

"No, it's not that," Caixiu shook her head. "That rooster..." she said, "I picked it from the brooder, fed it every day, and saw it grow bigger and bigger."

"That explains it. You raised it—that makes it harder for you to part with it." Mom cast an exploratory look at her and said, "It is already killed—what's done can't be undone, can it?"

Caixiu again shook her head, "No, it's not that." Mom waited for her to explain, but she hemmed and hawed, and finally said, "Even though you killed the rooster, you won't get much meat off of it. We don't really eat roosters in the countryside."

Mom sensed admonition from it—admonition from a country girl, of all people. Feeling a bit embarrassed, she quickly turned to walk away from Caixiu, while saying, "You have to listen to the rooster crow in the countryside, whereas we don't; we have the alarm clock. It's more beneficial to get the rooster marinated and cooked to eat!"

The rooster's luxuriant and beautiful feathers—which had been plucked out by my dad and spread out on old newspapers—were basking in the sun. Squatting in front of the feathers, Caixiu picked up a golden yellow one, pinched it, and put it down. "Why do you keep the rooster feathers?" she asked. "Is it for making shuttlecocks? Little brother, do you kick shuttlecocks?"

"Me? Of course not! I am no girl!" I told her testily, "Once sundried, they will be sold to the purchasing station. Rooster feathers can be sold for cash!"

After all, Caixiu was my family's guest. Whether we liked her or not, we bestowed on her the same courtesy, not one bit less. On the first day, my sister took Caixiu to visit the public park. However, she wasn't much into it, so they came out after taking a quick lap through it. "There is not much to see, just some big trees, a pond, a pavilion set up on some rockwork next to the pond—and you call it a park? And they charge admission?" Caixiu griped. Once out and seeing others all heading inside, she started to regret. "We shouldn't have hurried out," she said to my sister. "We can't get back the three-cent admission fee anyhow. We might just as well have stayed inside longer." According to my sister, Caixiu lamented wasting the three cents all the way back; only when they got to Dongfeng Photo Studio did she forget about the agony the park had inflicted upon her.

Standing at the entrance of the photo studio, Caixiu couldn't make her feet move, engrossed in browsing through the photos of beautiful girls in its display window. My sister also liked the photo display anyway, so she viewed them with her, patiently. Caixiu said she had never had a photo taken before and asked about the cost. My sister read her mind, but she was in a bind. "My mom gave me only one yuan—the allowance for your reception. It's only enough for a ½ inch x ½ inch photo, about the size of a fingernail," she said.

Caixiu held up her fingers to think it over. "Oh, that'd be too small to see, it would be a waste," she said. "Do they have any bigger size?"

"Of course they do, 1 inch x 1 inch and 2 inch x 2 inch," said my sister. "But you will have to pay the extra amount out of your own pocket. Do you have any money?"

Caixiu hesitated for a bit. She looked at the passersby and pulled my sister closer. "You shield me," she exhorted her. While shielding Caixiu with her body, my sister heard her busily fumbling under the drawstring of her pants. Finally, Caixiu fished out a roll of Jiao banknotes tied with a rubber band. "I've got money," she said, "I've got more money than any other girl in Gu Village."

They came back rather late only because they had been lining up in front of the studio to have their photos taken. Girls mostly appeared affected and stilted while posing for the camera in a photo studio. They still looked that way when they returned. Caixiu was wearing my sister's white embroidered shirt, her two long braids pulled up in a top-knot bun, like a lump of horse dung. Her hair now looked just like my sister's. She didn't wipe the lipstick completely off her lips—perhaps intentionally so—which looked bright red. She had the appearance of having just come off stage, somewhat excited, but also a little shy. As she wasn't clear what proofs were, I heard her repeatedly ask the same question: With that many girls having their photos taken, will the studio mistakenly give her photos to someone else, and vice versa?

"How could that be possible?" Being hounded with that single question, my sister got annoyed. "I've already told you over and over that you will show the proofs when picking up the photos," she said somewhat caustically. "Who would want someone else's photos? You are no beauty, why would somebody else want your photos?"

I was forced to spend five days with Caixiu. I didn't believe she was as simple as Dad said she was or as shrewd as Mom said she was. During those five days, Caixiu remained almost a complete mystery to me. For instance, I couldn't fathom why she ate so little at the table but then opened the cover of the dishes in the kitchen when no one was around. She ate the braised pork with arrowhead tubers, stealthily, like a thief; I saw it clearly—she dipped her fingers into the dish, pushed the tubers aside, plucked up the meat, and put it into her mouth. There's nothing peculiar about eating the dish secretly, which I did often myself. But the way she was holding our sugar jar in her arms and eating the white sugar out of it truly astounded me. So I shouted at her, "Hey, what are you doing here?!" Startled, she dropped the jar on the floor, which immediately broke into pieces; half a jar of sugar spilled out onto the floor.

Caixiu's face turned ghastly pale. She stood there woodenly, and it took her quite a while to recover from her fright. Once she did, she yelled, stomping her feet, "Look what you've done!"

I didn't expect she would make such a bogus accusation, so I screamed, "You were eating the sugar in secret—it's you! Look what *you've* done!"

"What have I done? There was a fly in the sugar jar, I got it out." She quickly calmed down. Kneeling on the floor, she carefully scooped the sugar into the cup of her hands and emptied it into a bowl. "I don't like sugar. Besides, I don't have eyes bigger than my belly." She raised her head and looked at me, her tone somewhat softer. "Even if my eyes were bigger than my belly, had you not frightened me, the jar wouldn't have dropped on the floor. So, little brother, you share some responsibility as well."

"I do not have any responsibility. It's all because you were secretly eating the sugar!"

She was no longer that flustered, her eyes sparkling—she must have been racking her brain, trying to think of a way out. "Auntie and the others are coming back home soon." She placed that bowl of sugar back on the wooden shelf and surveyed my face. "I will say I broke this jar of sugar due to carelessness. But little brother, you are not going to falsely accuse me of secretly eating the sugar. Be sure not to accuse me falsely, OK?"

"Who accused you falsely? I saw you eating it in secret." Suddenly, I felt a strong disdain and hatred toward this country girl. Something brutal blurted out of my mouth, "A man with epilepsy would make a fitting mate for the likes of you!"

Caixiu must never have expected such mean words from me. She stared at me in horror. "Who taught you to say such things?" her eyes flashed with fury.

I had a foreboding that she would make some dangerous move, but it was already too late for me to flee. Her throat emitted a gulp sound; she lowered her head, lurched toward my chest like a beast. I instantly lost my balance and plopped down on our water vat.

That was perhaps my only full frontal confrontation with Caixiu. That happening was neither fish nor fowl, with no loser or winner—

winning it would have been pointless, anyhow. I never spoke with Caixiu again after the sugar jar incident. Later, she must have regretted butting me in the chest with her head. When I was leaving for school, she affably helped me adjust my collar. I felt a loathing toward her hands and shook them off. She retreated aside with good grace and said, to comfort either me or herself, "That's all right. You are still a kid. That's all right." Of course I was all right. Except that whenever I walked past the bulletin board displays at school and saw Gong Ai-hua's photo, I would think of Caixiu. Which would make me feel that inside there was a hidden silhouette—in a prone position—of a strange man from the countryside, tongueless, foaming at the mouth. Thus, the bright bulletin board displays suddenly became spooky.

My sister brought back the proofs of her and Caixiu's photos. She and Caixiu were hiding in the attic and looking at them, as if holding a solemn, clandestine activity. I heard them laughing and larking around. Photos had brought my sister nothing but disgruntlement. She always felt that the photographer made her look ugly. As for Caixiu, she was pleasantly surprised by the 1 inch x 1 inch proof, which seemed not just about her looks, but perhaps even about her life. That day, I saw Caixiu come down from the attic, her dusky red face glowing with an incredulous joy. With such elation she was rubbing arrowhead tubers in the kitchen. My sister was changing the honeycomb briquette in the stove nearby. She suddenly thought of the man with epilepsy and turned back to Caixiu. "What is he like? Why is he called an epileptic?"

Caixiu kept silent for a while, as if waiting for my sister to take back such a question that would harm others without benefitting herself. Not only did my sister not withdraw her question, but she went even further, asking, "Does he hit people?"

This time, Caixiu answered unequivocally, "No, he doesn't. Why would he? One can only hope that others wouldn't hit him." She sounded unusually calm. "Have you ever seen a mad sheep? Just like a sheep sick with scrapie lying on the ground, cramping, shaking, and foaming at the mouth." Abruptly, Caixiu let out a hollow laugh, which quickly faded away. After a while, I heard her say in the kitchen, "Actually they're all muddle-headed. No matter whom I'm married to, there won't be a good life. If I were to marry him, it's not just hard on me... life would be harder for him." My sister couldn't follow that, so she was adamant about getting to the bottom of it. Caixiu threw the piece of porcelain onto the floor and stalked out of the kitchen—her hands covering her face—and back to the attic.

One day at dusk—I don't quite remember if it was the fourth or the fifth day Caixiu came to stay with us—she and my whole family were having dinner when in rushed Auntie, who waved her hand to Caixiu straight away, "Stop eating, stop eating. Hurry up, go! Go hide in the attic!"

As it turned out, Caixiu's elder brother, Changshou, had come for her. Apparently, Auntie wasn't prepared to handle an emergency like this. A cold sweat broke out on her scalp. She nudged Caixiu to the stairs leading to the attic. "Your brother scared me to death," she said. "He's squatting in front of my house, holding a chemical fertilizer bag with a thick hemp rope inside—he was coming to tie you up!"

Dad pounded the table and said, "Bringing a rope to tie up someone in broad daylight! Isn't there any law of the land? Seize him and turn him over to the police!" Everyone was furious about that thick hemp rope, but after the initial fury died down, they got somewhat nervous. After all, it was the domestic affair of their family, and that was no way to handle him. "Did he locate your home by following the house number?" Mom asked Auntie. "Is he going to squat in front of our house?" Auntie told Mom she could rest assured that Changshou wouldn't be able to identify our house, although he located hers. Mom wasn't convinced though. "I know too well you've got some really gossipy neighbors—they would readily volunteer the information."

Auntie repeatedly denied such a possibility, but deep inside she wasn't so sure herself. She grabbed a towel to wipe the beads of sweat that were springing out on her forehead. Suddenly, resentment flashed in her eyes. "Gong Aihua, it was all her doing!" Auntie cried out. "She's playing good Samaritan while leaving all the dirty work to others. How could she just freeload off of others like that? I don't care whether she's back or not, tomorrow I'm sending Caixiu to her family anyway. Changshou knows where my family's house is, and I know where her family's house is!"

All of a sudden, no one was taking any stand. Dad signaled Auntie to lower her voice, lest Caixiu—who was up in the attic—hear her. Auntie obliged, but said, with some trace of lingering resentment in her tone, "I'm not worried about her overhearing me. Considering that we're neither relatives nor friends to her, we've treated her well."

There was a sudden tense, agitated air on the usually peaceful Mahogany Street. Mom asked me to go out and take a look. I saw nobody outside. It was the big yellow dog from the blacksmith's family across the street that was squatting in front of our house. I looked east and saw a throng of human shadows in front of Auntie's house in the distance. Not sure if it was my blurry vision or my being overly vigilant, but I vaguely saw those figures all pointing toward my home.

By the time I walked back inside, Auntie had made up her mind. She was going to move Caixiu out of our home right away. "You've hosted her several days for me. I can't drag you all into this any further," said Auntie. "Those country folks are hardly reasonable. In case her brother comes and causes trouble or even some unfortunate incident, I would fail your family."

"Are you sending her to Gong Aihua's home right now?" Mom asked. "Gong Aihua hasn't got back yet, has she?"

"Undue delay may cause trouble. I'm worrying about the loose lips of Granny Shaoxing and Aunty Qian. I'll have to send her there anyhow, might as well do it now rather than later," Auntie replied. "If Gong Aihua is not home, so be it—what's the big deal? Aren't parents supposed to take the fall for their children? It's not that I'm cold-hearted, I just want fairness. It's now Gong Aihua's parents' turn to take care of Caixiu!"

Auntie wheeled out Dad's bike. She insisted on going herself, by bike—with Caixiu on its back seat—to Gong Aihua's home in Little Willow Alley. She had to go anyway, as she was the only one who knew where Gong Aihua's family lived. Mom and Auntie talked through the bike route options—how to bypass Auntie's house to hoodwink others—and they agreed that cutting through the oil and fat processing factory would be the most scientific route. Mom dug out a pair of blue overalls, for Caixiu to put on, just to be on the safe side. Then I heard Auntie calling Caixiu's name at the bottom of the stairs. "Caixiu, Caixiu, come down," she said. "We are leaving for Gong Aihua's home." It was silent up in the attic. Auntie called again, "Caixiu, Caixiu, come down here. It's safest to go to Gong Aihua's home. Your brother won't be able to find you there." Caixiu's silence prompted everyone to gather around the stairs, all heads looking up anxiously.

"Caixiu, it's not that we're afraid of getting into trouble. We are doing this for your own good," said Mom. "Your brother came with a rope. You're blood siblings no matter what. We're caught in the middle of your family affairs; it's pretty tricky for us."

Auntie appeared quite snappish. "Caixiu, hurry down here, will you? Your brother will be here any time now," she said, tapping the stair railing with the bike key. "Once he shows up, you won't be able to get away even if you want to. We'll have no choice but to see him tie you up and take you back to your village." In her irritable state, Auntie sounded as if she were beguiling a young child. She was no longer aiming her spear at Gong Aihua; instead, she was exaggerating the benefits of her home. "Gong Aihua's home is in a zigzagging small alley. Your brother won't be able to find it," she said. "Her home is right next to a police station. Besides, she's a well-publicized model figure. If your brother dares to make a scene at her home, the police will go get him!"

Caixiu was getting down from the attic, her face taut. It was hard to tell whether she had cried—she was lowering her eyes all the time. She had the kind of solemn expression one would assume after being ashamed, or perhaps the kind of relaxed expression one would wear after the releasing of sorrows. I noticed her chin was wet. Carrying her gray PVC leather gripsack, she walked down slowly. Until the last step of the stairs, when she suddenly dropped her bag, clutching her stomach, and sat down.

My sister ran up to support her. "Caixiu, do you have stomachache?"

Caixiu nodded first, but then she shook her head when she saw Mom had already stretched open the overalls. She pushed my sister aside and stood up herself, standing there like a stick. They helped her put on the overalls with much hurry and bustle. Gazing closely at her, my sister said, "Go look at yourself in the mirror, Caixiu. You look completely different now!"

Mom and Auntie both opposed her suggestion, "Oh, you trouble-maker. This is no time to look in the mirror!"

Even in the overalls, Caixiu was still Caixiu. She remained silent; thus, no one knew what was on her mind. Next, Caixiu followed behind the bike Auntie was wheeling, and we were right behind her—our whole party got out onto the street very cautiously. Looking east, the shadows in front of Auntie's house had thickened quite a bit—a sign that the risk of having the secret divulged was increasing. "Hurry up!" Caixiu was almost held up onto the bike seat by us all.

Not until she was sitting on the bike did I realize why she appeared somewhat unhinged in her departure. "Photos! Photos!" abruptly she turned back and shouted at my sister. "My photos, how will you give them to me?"

That night, sure enough, Changshou came in front of our house. He knocked on the door. When no one answered, he started pounding the door with his fist, while shouting, "Caixiu, come on out! Come the hell out!" After some time, Dad went to open the door, not to let Changshou in, but to get himself out and call on his people for help. Dad stepped over that fertilizer bag calmly; casting a glance at the rope in it, he sneered, "Huh, you've brought the rope to tie up someone. We will see who will get bound in the end."

By the time I got out of bed, Dad's people had arrived. A sizable crowd of men, among them some elders, who came to help with persuasion, and several friends of my cousin—some good-for-nothing sloths, all burly and beefy; one would know what they were there for just by looking at them. Those sloths pulled Changshou out the door, as they spat curses at him, "You country bumpkin, sold your younger sister like livestock, and still you dared to come here to make trouble! If I were you, I would bash my head against a block of tofu and die!"

Changshou was short but stout. He was carried out of our house through the doorway, but being bullheaded, he quickly made his way back in. "Caixiu, Caixiu, come the hell out!" He was pushed to the ground. Yet he firmly grabbed onto the doorframe with one hand, struggling to get back in. He kept calling his sister's name, not minding others' curses one bit, nor did he rebut them. The dim yellow light was shining in his face; it looked strikingly similar to Caixiu's—square-shaped, with a flat nose, but big, bright eyes. This melee went on for quite a while. At last, Changshou became quiet. He had to. When his drawstring fell out, the sloths seized the chance to pull his pants halfway down.

"If you don't stop, we will send you to the police like this and have them detain you for committing hooliganism!" they said to him menacingly. Changshou was desperately holding his pants up, and finally quieting down. The sloths, however, couldn't stop themselves. They pushed him around, and began to curse him again, "If you were unable to get yourself a wife, you could have just managed to do without. There're so many pigs and sheep in the countryside, can't you just go f--- the sows and the ewes? Why did you trade your sister to that much older epileptic? Here, take back your drawstring. Go hang yourself!"

Changshou didn't retort, his eyes evading those several young men, as if their cuss words were kind of true. He ignored the elders' ideological and moral persuasion, as though they were persuading themselves. Sitting on the ground, he noticed one shoe had fallen off his foot. He pushed and shoved others' legs around, one after another, looking for his other green canvas "liberation shoe". That shoe was right behind Dad. Changshou leaned forward to pick it up. One of the sloths, of quick eye and deft hand, moved swiftly to get hold of it and threw it far away. "Go pick it up. You're not allowed to return here!" The sloth gave Changshou a push. "Walk east to get to the long-distance bus station. Spend the night there and catch the bus at the crack of dawn. Get the hell back to where you came from!"

That shoe appeared very important to Changshou, and it showed. We saw Changshou standing next to the sloth and staring at him angrily. "Why are you staring at me? That dirty and smelly shoe?" said the sloth, "If you don't hurry up to get it, the dog will gnaw on it as sh-t." Changshou pushed him tentatively. The sloth laughed him down, "You dared to push me! You wanna refuse a toast only to be forced to drink a forfeit? Cut it out, or else I will throw you away! Try it, I dare you!"

Changshou went off to pick up that shoe. He was walking bow-legged; he seemed to be struggling along, or perhaps having some joint pain. We watched him go to pick up his shoe. Dad felt a bit uneasy and said to the sloth, "It's enough for you to scare him off. Why did you treat him rough like that?"

"Hayseeds of his kind need to be subject to dictatorship of the proletariat; there's no other way to subdue him," the sloth replied. "When he's back, I will continue to freak him out."

Everyone expected Changshou to come back after picking up his shoe. But to the surprise of all, he just paused a while in the distance, before he actually started to walk east. He walked very slowly. The shadow of a diminutive figure was drifting, little by little, in the lamplight along Mahogany Street. Just when everybody believed Changshou had been fully subdued, all of a sudden, a forlorn shriek exploded somewhere in the far background, "Caixiu, Caixiu, come the hell out!"

Again he started calling his sister's name, only this time along the street deep at night. Thus, his voice, with a bleak echo, sounded a bit scary. I well remember that I could faintly hear Changshou getting choked up, but the pitiful sobbing was quickly followed, yet again, by that terrifying roar, "Caixiu, Caixiu, come the hell out, follow me home!"

Several days later, my sister delivered the photos to Little Willow Alley. She tried every possible way to find Gong Aihua's home. When she finally found it, however, she didn't get to meet Gong Aihua, or Caixiu. She only met Gong Aihua's elderly grandma through the kitchen window.

Gong Aihua's grandma happened to be rubbing arrowhead tubers in the kitchen. According to my sister, at first glance she recognized they were tubers from Gu Village—plump, round, with pink tails. Seeing tubers from Gu Village was tantamount to seeing the person from Gu Village. But my sister wasn't able to get Gong Aihua down after calling out her name. The hair of Gong Aihua's grandma was a hoary white. Perhaps she was a dotard, or she was just shrewd. As my sister looked in from outside the window, she quietly watched, keeping a close eye on her. And only when my sister called Gong Aihua's name did she stand up, shakily. "Don't be so loud. Some neighbors working the night shift are still sleeping," through the window she hastily gestured to my sister with her hand. "Aihua isn't in. She's a busy bee, off to the provincial capital for meetings again!"

According to my sister, she saw the face of a young lady with short hair flashing across the window upstairs. She suspected that it was Gong Aihua. Moreover, a white bra of the style for young ladies hung on the drying pole that stretched out from the window and was still dripping water. That deepened her suspicion. She couldn't fathom why Gong Aihua wasn't home. She had no choice but to ask about Caixiu's whereabouts from the old lady, who became even more vigilant. "Who are you? Where did you come from?" she asked my sister.

Such simple questions caught my sister off guard. She couldn't explain who she was. In a fit of pique she tossed Caixiu's photos onto the table next to the window. "I'm not gonna meddle in others' business. I came here only to deliver the photos." Now that the photos were thrown inside, my sister became somewhat concerned. Returning to the window, she stretched out her hands inside, fumbled out one photo from the small paper sleeve while blocking the old lady's view. "It's no cinch to have the photos taken," she said. "With the kind of attitude your family has, I'm worried. I'm gonna keep one for her."

Right before my sister left, she heard the latest on Caixiu—revealed by Gong Aihua's grandma. On the matter of Caixiu, apparently the old lady was biased, or she completely misunderstood the role Gong Aihua played in it. Through the window she scolded my sister, "Stop using our Aihua as cannon fodder and coming to her for whatever trouble you run into. Is she supposed to be responsible for the girl's marriage as well? You all harbor evil design—can't bear to see her advancing, and intentionally hinder her future career!" My sister wasn't able to make head nor tail of the accusations. She was standing there, rolling her eyes at the old lady, who became resentful and threw out an arrowhead tuber tail. "Stop rolling your eyes at me," she said. "Our Aihua isn't in charge of that country girl's affairs, the Women's Federation is. If you want to find the girl, go to the Women's Federation!"

Thus, it was my sister who brought back the news that Caixiu had gone to the Women's Federation. Later on, we got to know that Caixiu indeed had been to the municipal office of the Women's Federation. It was Gong Aihua's father who took her there. He was a government cadre himself, and he knew best which agencies would solve what types of problems, and which ones would have the authority to do what, and so on. And yet apparently, the Women's Federation in our city couldn't fix her problem in a short period of time. Thus, Gong Aihua's father asked Caixiu to report her situation in detail to the cadres there. He was eager to report to work, so he drew a sketch map to his house, and told her to find her own way back there. They said that day, Caixiu was sitting in the office of the Women's Federation for a very long time, and she also talked for a very long time. Others weren't aware that she was talking about her own circumstances; it sounded as though she were describing someone else's horrible marriage. Later, she was escorted out of the office.

She didn't immediately leave, though. Instead, she sat quietly on a long bench, listening to a couple who sought a divorce calling each other names in the hallway and exposing the details of each other's private lives. She went up to try to calm down the wife—as to what she said, others just couldn't follow. Some time later, the office closed, and the cadres all left. While passing the Iron Lion Bridge, a female cadre with the office's reception section saw that girl from Gu Village sitting beneath one end of the bridge—she was looking around and comparing the sketch map on a sheet of letter paper with her physical surroundings, while drinking a one-cent cup of hot tea. The cadre went to buy a bag of polished long-grain rice from the rice trading boat beneath the bridge. When she returned, she glanced at the tea stall. Caixiu was still sitting there. By this point, however, her sorrows had gushed out like the morning sun. She was crying, holding the cup of tea, while watching the people coming and going across the bridge. The tea stand owner and several warm-hearted passersby went up to stand around her. They had thought the country girl was crying because of the letter. But once the paper was spread out, what they saw was a simple sketch map drawn with a ballpoint pen. The cadre hesitated for a while, but in the end she hurried off to go home and cook dinner. Because she heard someone come forward gallantly and say, "Little Willow Alley? I know where it is, let me take you there!"

Now we all know how it turned out—that compassionate person didn't actually take Caixiu back to Gong Aihua's home. It was an inscrutable outcome. Even now, those parties concerned are still debating who that person offering to lead the way was and where on earth he took Caixiu. Thereafter, being unable to find his sister, Changshou created some disturbances at Gong Aihua's home for several days. But the whole time he didn't see any trace of Caixiu; Gong Aihua didn't make an appearance, either. Nevertheless, the police showed up. In accordance with certain rules, they carted Changshou off to the long-distance bus station and sent him back home.

None of us ever saw Caixiu again. One day, as soon as my sister came back home, she told Mom she saw a missing-person poster for Caixiu. "Caixiu is missing, so it's natural to have the poster put up," Mom said. But my sister started crying.

"That photo, that photo!" she blurted out. Sudden understanding dawned on Mom's face, which turned pale.

"Now you are crying, but when I asked you to take her out for the day, somehow you took her to have the photos taken. Why did you do that? Why? What's the point of having photos taken? Huh? What for?" Questioning my sister impulsively, Mom burst into tears herself. Their reasoning led logically to a grim conclusion—my sister couldn't get away with it, and therefore Mom bore a heavy moral burden. To release the pressure, Mom inevitably held Auntie accountable. One can easily imagine how it all ended. Mom and Auntie cut ties with each other. Our two families lived close by, both on Mahogany Street. Auntie is Dad's blood younger sister, Dad is Auntie's blood elder brother. But just like that, our two families broke off the relationships.

Later on, Caixiu was seen taking a ride on an arrowhead tuber trading boat back to Gu Village. That piece of information was verified. Which made us all—both mine and Auntie's family—happy, for a while. Still, we knew nothing about the several days when Caixiu had disappeared—where, how, and with whom she spent those few days; the details will forever remain an unsolved mystery.

According to my cousin, later, Caixiu did fulfill her family's commitment and married that middle-aged man with epilepsy. When my cousin returned home for the Spring Festival, he mentioned that their marriage appeared just fine. He saw Caixiu and her husband go to the farmers' market. She bought baby chickens and he got a hoe; they were walking on the road, one trailing behind the other. But when my cousin came back during the May Day holiday, he made no mention of Caixiu. When pressed, he revealed the shocking news that Caixiu had committed suicide by drinking pesticide. My cousin said Caixiu had planned well for her own death: "She was spraying pesticide on the vegetable field. After she was done, others saw her holding a plastic barrel and sitting in the field. They all thought she was drinking water and asked her, 'Caixiu, we saw you just had water. Why have you become thirsty again so soon?' 'It's hot today. I'm dying of thirst,' Caixiu replied. Caixiu drank half a barrel of pesticide in front of many people." Both Auntie's family and mine were horrified. My cousin mentioned, somewhat evasively and vaguely, some rumors circulating in the village that Caixiu was probably pregnant when she died, and that people suspected the baby was a bastard, not the epileptic's.

Auntie immediately cried out, "Epilepsy doesn't affect one's fertility. If it wasn't his, who else's can it be?"

Then we all fell silent. Everyone's mind turned to the time period when Caixiu went missing and the fact that she returned to Gu Village with a secret. No one dared speak. Everybody was trying to conceal their fluster but could hardly hide their guilty expressions. Then all of a sudden, Auntie stood up, uttering some words, which made us all feel relieved. "We have a clear conscience in this matter about Caixiu. Hers was a hard lot—can't really blame others for that," she said. "If someone has to be blamed, it should be Gong Aihua. Had she not meddled in it and invited the trouble, things wouldn't have ended so badly for Caixiu."

Residents of the Mahogany Street area were accustomed to placing the photos of relatives and friends under the glass table cover. That photo of Caixiu had been put under the glass cover of our bureau. In that spot usually stood a vase of artificial flowers, which covered up Caixiu's photo year in and year out, as if covering up something private that we could not discard nor would we want to expose. We went about our ordinary, mundane, everyday lives filled with trivialities; who would think of a country girl from Gu Village for no apparent reason? We almost forgot about Caixiu, until that time when we moved. My sister and I were sorting through the photos under the glass cover when we suddenly spotted the one of Caixiu. For a moment, we simply couldn't remember who the person in the photo was. I was trying to peel the photo off the glass that it had stuck to, wondering who it was and why it looked so familiar. Suddenly, my sister called out, "It's Caixiu! How come her photo is still down here?"

I, too, remembered Caixiu. I wasn't sure why, but whenever I thought of Caixiu, I would think of arrowhead tubers. As a child, I didn't like to eat them, but somehow I enjoyed braised pork with arrowhead tubers. A middle-aged man now, I have stopped eating arrowhead tubers and braised pork with arrowhead tubers too.

STUART DISCHELL
The Greatness of Thomas Lux: A Look2 Essay

Reading a prolific writer is like visiting a big city. In Thomas Lux, readers find their own districts. For some it is his literary and historical poems or his obsession with maps or language itself that runs throughout his oeuvre, or the poems of social satire, like "The Happy Majority" or "The Nazi at the Puppet Show." For others it is the work that hints at the spiritual world in *God Particles* or the gorgeous odes in his last book with its now prophetic title *To the Left of Time*. Because I am his friend, I treasure his poems of family life. I have always admired the way he could make consequence, and ultimately literary figure, out of maraschino cherries in a boyhood refrigerator, the skates hung on the wall along the basement stairs, or his parents' sugar spoon worn "until it's almost flimsy as tinfoil." And then there are the many poems, some odd nursery rhyme–like constructions, inspired by the birth of his daughter, Claudia, an event that made his heart, as well as his imagination, expand.

Thomas Lux's death on February 5, 2017, came as a shock to his friends in the many places in which he lived and taught and to his worldwide readership. At seventy, with shoulder-length blond hair, blue jeans, quick smile, gorgeous shirts, and his wisecracking, sometimes rebellious, manner, he still cut the figure of a young poet and retained a youthful and joyous vitality. A reverent irreverent, he never wavered in his love of the making and teaching of poetry and lived his life faithful to the first principles of his art. He believed deeply in poetry, its capacity to change people's lives. He was our natural laureate. And he would have made a wise old man.

Thomas Lux grew up on a dairy farm in Easthampton, Massachusetts. His uncle tended the cows; his father delivered the milk. His mother worked for the telephone company. An only child, he followed the Red Sox and was bookish in his teens, a habit he continued throughout his life. Anyone who has ever been to one of his residences has seen the mile-high stacks of new poetry books and the hardbound volumes of all kinds, usually nonfiction, from which he harvested his odd facts. On the farm he read adventure books, histories, and biographies. He learned to shoot and he rode a horse named Sunday, thus, the title for his third book of poems.

Because he lived his entire adult life in cities or just outside them, the landscape of Western Massachusetts always remained an important touchstone like the Heaney cattle farm in Derry or the Roethke greenhouse in Michigan. For him the dairy farm was a lifelong "cradle place" of love and sanity. Throughout his poetry, he reconstructs the farm in numerous works, such as the early poem "Barnfire," in which, "because they know they are safe there, / the horses run back into the barn," or in "The Voice You Hear," wherein "the barn you say / is a barn you know or knew," or in Lux's newest book, *To the Left of Time*, which is filled with references, among them a titular "Milking Stool." In Lux's popular *New and Selected Poems: 1975-1995*, he writes:

> It happened that my uncle liked to take my hand in his
> and with the other seize
> the electric cow fence: a little rural
> humor, don't get me wrong
> ("Triptych, Middle Panel Burning")

Lux's family life gave him an ethos and decency that formed the greater aesthetic of his poetry: a celebration of the flawed but deeply loved, and a gratitude for the life given him.

The Lux-icon has many vivid expressions and affectionate names for things. His book *Memory's Handgrenade* became "Memory's Hand-Job"; Houghton Mifflin was "the muffler"; Cleveland State University Press was "Cheapland State," Ploughshares "the Plow-Boy," and so on. These appellations were never meant to be insulting; he was always enormously grateful to his publishers and editors and wrote one of his best elegies to Peter Davison, his longtime editor at Houghton Mifflin and *The Atlantic*. Nicknames were part of the fun that made it easy to be around him. Fatherhood gave him a tendency to add an *ie* onto words—so maybe we would go get a "drinkie" after a reading. One thing he did not care for when his name was used professionally was being referred to as Tom Lux rather than Thomas Lux. He once told me, "No one puts up a poster or prints your name as Stu Dischell."

Lux's relationship to Emerson College and the Plow-Boy goes back to his undergraduate days. In a profile I wrote for Ploughshares issue 77 (Winter 1998-99) for which Lux edited the poetry, I interviewed James Randall, one of the early spirits behind Ploughshares, the first director of Emerson's MFA Program, and Lux's first publisher at Pym-Randall Press. When I asked him what Lux was like as a college student, he told me: "In the late 1960s when Lux came to us, the writing program was new. He looked vaguely like a hobo in dress and manner, but he stayed on. There was a freshness and openness about him, and he spread his enthusiasms to others. Before we knew it, we had a serious poetry group at our college." Upon graduation Randall hired him as Emerson's poet-in-residence. Lux then spent a year studying at Iowa before coming back to teach for several years at Emerson. He also served as an advisory editor to Ploughshares and guest-edited three issues.

In his long career at Sarah Lawrence College and then for the last dozen years at the Georgia Institute of Technology where he held an honorary professorship, the Bourne Chair in Poetry, Lux taught thousands of students, if you include stints at Boston University, Columbia University, the University of Houston, the University of Iowa Writers' Workshop, the University of California at Irvine, University of Michigan, Oberlin College, and in the Warren Wilson low-residency MFA Program for Writers. The list of those he continued to mentor is huge as well. He loved teaching and frequently remarked, "Can you believe they pay us for this?" or "Beats the hell out of working in the box factory." He told his wife, poet Jennifer Holley Lux, that he "wanted to be dragged feet-first out of the classroom." He nearly succeeded, having taught until a few months before he died.

Sometimes I think our Thomas was an angel of some kind, but he was not a saint. On more than one occasion, he quieted a gallery or bar venue by telling people to "shut the fuck up" when someone else's reading was being disturbed. He had a temper when people were rude to others, especially to working people. I was thrilled when he got mad like that. But he was cool without knowing it—as truly cool people never know how cool they are. I can recount again how the first night we hung out together in 1981, we met up with Franz Wright, whom he had taught at Oberlin, at the Bow and Arrow in Cambridge, a true dive bar. I remember walking past the bouncer who worked the door and him shouting after us, "Hey, Mick Jagger, it's Mick Jagger, man." Lux's smile had the bite of mischief; being "mis-chee-vi-ous," he willfully pronounced the word. In the early pictures, such as the one on the cover of *Sunday*, you can see a little smirk of skepticism there too. That was the smile that scared people who were full of shit. Later, the smile became broader, gentler, without hesitation, and had a contagious quality for those around him.

He could also be fiercely critical concerning poets of needless or pedantic obscurity and their use of the kinds of abstractions and allusions that make readers feel bad about themselves, the writers who struck their knowledge like a club against the audience. Instead, he loved to find the historical detail that told a story: "Walt Whitman's Brain Dropped on Laboratory Floor," "Hitler's Slippers," or a scientific fact like river blindness were ways to invite the reader in. He also invented imaginative details to engender poems such as "Jesus' Baby Teeth" or "The Deathwatch Beetle." His curiosity was as endless as his reading and attentiveness. The surrealism of his early poetry had itself transformed into a metaphoric way of seeing.

Although not as formal a poet as his early influences Hart Crane and Theodore Roethke, Lux's great gifts are in his ability to create surprise and unpredictability through the syntactical construction of the sentence as it breaks against the line: the genius of his free verse, which offers greater possibility for enjambments than the metered line yet produces musicality. The Thomas Lux poem accumulates power through its vertical movement down the page; the poem is always on the move. I imagine this is why Lux wrote nearly all of his later poems in a single stanza structure, so as not to showcase or showboat the linguistic dexterity. A good example of this is the opening lines of "A Small Tin Parrot Pin."

> Next to the tiny bladeless windmill
> of a salt shaker
> on the black tablecloth
> is my small tin parrot pin,
> bought from a bin,
> 75 cents, cheap, not pure tin—an alloy,
> some plastic toy tin?
> The actual pin, the pin that pins the pin,
> will fall off soon

and thus the parrot
if I wear it, which I will
on my lapel. I'll look down
and it'll be gone.

Language itself is a subject he returns to, itself evident in titles like
"Virgule," "Amphibrach Dance," and "The Oxymoron Sisters." Lux's
syntactical genius, along with unpredictable inclusions of diction, particularly his love of nouns, especially proper nouns, gives him some
of the most varied diction of poets of his generation. The reader need
only open a book at random to find titles like "The Grand Climacteric"
face-à-face with "Vaticide."

One of my favorites of his poems has its own history with
Ploughshares; it was published in the Fall 1979 issue, and later reprinted
as the first poem in the chapbook *Massachusetts: Ten Poems*, published
by James Randall in the Pym-Randall Press series. Ultimately, "The
Milkman and His Son" appears as the first poem in his important book
Half Promised Land, when his poetry was developing from a period
surrealism into finding transformation in the quirky human round of
daily activity.

The Milkman and His Son

For a year he'd collect
the milk bottles—those cracked,
chipped, or with the label's blue
scene of a farm

fading. In winter
they'd load the boxes on a sled
and drag them to the dump

which was lovely then: a white sheet
drawn up, like a joke, over
the face of a sleeper.
As they lob the bottles in

the son begs a trick

and the milkman obliges: tossing
one bottle in a high arc
he shatters it in midair

with another. One thousand
astonished splints of glass
falling...Again
and again, and damned
if that milkman,

that easy slinger
on the dump's edge (as the drifted
junk tips its hats

of snow) damned if he didn't
hit almost half! Not bad.
Along with gentleness,

and the sane bewilderment
of understanding nothing cruel,
it was a thing he did best.

In my copy of *Massachusetts: Ten Poems,* on the state map on the title page, he drew an arrow and circled a dot he made where he lived in Easthampton. He wrote: "Tom's House." The inscription is dated December 10, 1981: his thirty-fifth birthday, though I did not know it at the time.

It is a fitting metaphor for our friendship that he would give me a gift without revealing it was his birthday. He gave constantly; Thomas Lux was not one to turn down a request for a letter of recommendation or paragraph of advance praise when requested for such, especially by a young poet. He dedicated many of his creative hours to this because he believed it would be wrong not to help someone who was talented and needed a break. "Dee or Disch or Dog," he would say. (His daughter, the novelist Claudia Kilbourne Lux, told me I'm called Dog in his extensive daybooks.) His generosity extended from friends and former students to random down-on-their-luck people who asked us for money on the streets of Boston or New York or Atlanta. Then there were times of extravagance when, celebrating his NEA grant at the Wursthaus in old Harvard Square, he gave the waitress a hundred-dollar tip on our fifty-dollar meal. She sure appreciated it.

On his deathbed, Thomas Lux was more concerned about the fate of *Flying into Myself,* Bill Knott's selected poems, which he had edited and were just about to appear, than *To the Left of Time*, his own new book of poems. I think the book is one of Lux's best. In a prescient way it is kind of a "selected" anthology—but not of poems already written as much as poems with his kinds of wide-ranging subjects. The title itself is richly suggestive and made more mysterious since Lux's passing.

Structured in three sections, the collection opens with a group of poems in which he revisits the landscapes of Western Massachusetts in "Cow Chases Boys," "Haystack of Needles," "Manure Pile Covered in Snow," and people with odd occupations such as "dowsers" and pre-occupations such as "The Horse Poisoner." The second part is a sequence of twenty-five odes and anti-odes to "joyful ones," "chronic insolvency," "scars," and "lichen," among other subjects. Lux uses the structure of the modern ode as if he had invented it and the poems together compose one longer intricate ode of thanks and gratitude. The third section forms an aggregate of elegies and oddities, poems of language itself, like "There's a Word for It" and "Onomatomania." Attila the Hun, Crazy Horse, and Pope Leo are here too. Notably, in "Frank Stanford at 63," he summons the poet whom he elegized nearly forty years earlier in *Sunday*:

> There's still a hole, Frank, a dented molecule
> a cracked genome in the poetry of America
> you were meant to fill, to make
> disappear...

Rereading the five books Thomas Lux published after *New and Selected Poems: 1975-1995* for this essay, I realized that one must stand back from a friend to see their greatness and the complexity of the work. A poet known for his wildness, Lux wrote most of his work in traditional structures—the elegy, the ode, and the pastoral—if not in traditional forms. Although elements of narrative appear in his poems, his writing is resolutely lyrical. His lines are not metrical yet are frequently accentual. There is a musical pulse that is darn near electric. His timing is perfect. Through countless poems he militates against injustice without posturing or self-aggrandizement. Tom would not have allowed that kind of admiration anyway—from me or anyone else. He would have wisecracked and thrown in a few choice expletives in a syntax that made each come alive as if you had never heard those words before.

His deflecting manner turned his attention to others, and he enjoyed listening to their stories; from the athlete-poets he loved to teach at Georgia Tech to former students who subsequently won major awards for their work, Thomas Lux influenced them all. He made them want to be poets, despite the groans of many a parent. Moreover, he created communities wherever he went. An able advocate for poetry, he edited the Barn Dream Press and Jeanne Duval Editions, created the MFA Program at Sarah Lawrence, along with Jean Valentine, began the Sarah Lawrence Summer Literary Seminars, and founded Poetry @ TECH. Lux was ever the writer and teacher who opened students' eyes to poetry, whether in the university classroom, a community workshop, a high-school library, a writers' conference, or at any of his readings. He brought poetry to life because he brought life to poetry: public life, family life, and the life of the imagination. He also made it OK to feel a little goofy in this world, like the man who "risked his life to write the words" he misspells in Lux's famous poem "I love You Sweatheart." People respond to that.

Over the course of his life, Lux gave over a thousand poetry readings at campuses throughout the country, bookstores, galleries, and festival stages. He also performed in Mexico, Ireland, Great Britain, and Germany. He was a remarkable reader of his poems with exact syntactical timing, intensity, and sometimes deadpan humor. No one was ever bored at a Thomas Lux reading when he woke the audience up with a poem like "The People of the Other Village," broke them up with "To Help the Monkey Cross the River," or broke their hearts with "Render, Render." (Fortunately, there are many fine recordings of him today on YouTube.) Everywhere he read, he expanded the audience for poetry.

Throughout his life, Thomas Lux made his "pals" into his sisters and brothers. In "For My Sister" from *To the Left of Time,* he addresses the sibling he never had: "Forever we've never spoken," he opens, and has occasion to inform his imagined sister of the death of their parents and the details of their decline. "Mother starved to death in truth. / For many months she could not swallow...Father did not know what to do / When his legs were lost beneath him." There is both remarkable intimacy and great distance—impossible distance here in the voice. How Luxian to turn a thing inside out to love it more and see it better. How fortunate, my friend, to write one of your best books last.

> and everyone knows that nothing is really real
> until it is written.
> Even those who don't read
> know that.
> ("Onomatomania")

Ann Beattie recommends *Movie Stars* by Jack Pendarvis (Dzanc Books, 2016). "The humor, and the (forgive me) world view in these stories makes me think of Robert Plunket. No one else would conclude a story with the dog looking out the window, 'white forepaws on the window ledge, safely behind the glass, staring at the cat with sick superiority.'"

Robert Boswell recommends *All the Dreams We've Dreamed: A Story of Hoops and Handguns on Chicago's West Side* by Rus Bradburd (Chicago Review Press, May 2018). "A deeply personal story of gun violence in Chicago among a network of people connected to basketball. It could not be more timely. Terrific book."

Peter Ho Davies recommends *Half Gods* by Akil Kumarasamy (Farrar, Straus and Giroux, June 2018). "A debut collection of interlinked stories that read like classics (the title itself nods back to the *Mahabharata*). The quiet gravity of these pieces—one about an immigrant butcher

in New Jersey comes to mind in particular—is profoundly affecting."

Lauren Groff recommends *Conversations with Friends* by Sally Rooney (Hogarth, 2017). "This is one of the wittiest novels I read in 2017, and it has stayed with me for months into the new year. Sally Rooney is still quite young, but already deeply accomplished, and I can't wait to see what she writes next."

Jane Hirshfield recommends *The Carrying* by Ada Limón (Milkweed, August 2018). "Ada Limón's precise music, clarity of image, and signature inhabitance of the imaginative and actual realms offer once again, in this new book, confirmation: Limón is a vital presence in the landscape of current American poems, a poet continually expanding the canvas."

Jane Hirshfield recommends *The Beekeeper* by Dunya Mikhail (New Directions, March 2018). "I have long admired Dunya Mikhail as a poet. In *The Beekeeper*, English-language readers may discover for the first time Dunya Mikhail as a journalist equally astonishing in her powers. This harrowing book, consummately constructed and written, presents the stories of a number of Yazidi Iraqi women, imprisoned by Daesh; of the local beekeeper who helps some of them escape; and of Mikhail's own experience, as a person fully present to the events she brings into words, as a person fully present to her own life."

Robert Pinsky recommends *Fort Necessity* by David Gewanter (The University of Chicago Press, February 2018). "A truly unique, unified, penetrating book of poems about our time, using documentary material with the verve of art."

Robert Pinsky recommends Carol Muske's *Blue Rose* (Penguin Poets, April 2018). "Intense focus, gorgeous music, a demonstration that the perspectives of gender can be expansive, increasing the range of feeling and subject."

Gerald Stern recommends *R E D* by Chase Berggrun (Birds, LLC, May 2018). "*R E D* is a single long poem of erasure derived from Bram Stoker's *Dracula*. I find it to be a deeply moving book that deals essentially with the abuse of women and male power run amok. The language is

lovely and the narrative, though it is a book of poetry, is as clear and ineluctable as a novel. It is highly readable and, as I say, original."

Gerald Stern recommends *Amerika* by Franz Kafka (Kurt Wolff, 1927). "*Amerika*, the title given by Max Brod, Kafka's literary executor, to his early unfinished novel written in 1912, is a kind of *bildungsroman* and picaresque novel, which reminds me of *Augie March* and many other such novels. It is a story of a sixteen-year-old boy's adventures in the New World. It is unfinished and ends with a proposed trip to a place called 'Oklahoma.' It anticipates the two later famous novels of Kafka's, *The Trial* and *The Castle*."

Gerald Stern recommends *Forest Dark* by Nicole Krauss (Harper Collins, 2017). "This is a fantasy in which Kafka does not die at the age of forty in 1924, but secretly moves to Palestine, which in the '30s was a British mandate, and it imagines Kafka continuing to write and live in obscurity in his later years, in Israel itself."

Dan Wakefield recommends *Silver Girl* by Leslie Pietrzyk (The Unnamed Press, February

2018). "A rich, full, no-holds-barred novel of the struggles of a young woman from a small-town, Midwestern, financially stressed family to coexist with her diamond-studded roommate at a snobby university and fight her way to sexual and intellectual adulthood."

EDITORS' CORNER
New Work by Former Guest Editors

Elizabeth Spires, *A Memory of the Future*, poems
(W. W. Norton & Company, July 2018)

Dan Wakefield (coeditor with Jerome Klinkowitz), *Kurt Vonnegut Complete Stories* (Seven Stories Press, 2017)

CONTRIBUTORS' NOTES

Wendell Berry's newest book is *The Art of Loading Brush: New Agrarian Writings* (Counterpoint, 2017). His book *Port William Novels & Stories (The Civil War to World War II)* was published this year by Library of America.

Belle Boggs is the author of *The Art of Waiting: On Fertility, Medicine, and Motherhood* (Graywolf, 2016) and *Mattaponi Queen* (Graywolf, 2010), a collection of linked stories set along Virginia's Mattaponi River. Her first novel, *The Gulf*, will be published in April 2019 by Graywolf Press. She teaches in the MFA program at North Carolina State University, and her work has been supported by fellowships from the NEA, the North Carolina Arts Council, and the Bread Loaf and Sewanee Writers' Conferences.

Robert Cohen is the author of five books of fiction, among them *Amateur Barbarians* (Scribner, 2009), *Inspired Sleep* (Vintage, 2009), and *The Varieties of Romantic Experience* (Vintage, 2002), and the coeditor of a recent anthology, *The Writer's Reader* (Bloomsbury, 2017). "Roaming Charges" has been excerpted from *Evening's Empire,* a novel in progress. Cohen teaches at Middlebury College and the Warren Wilson MFA Program.

Carrie Cooperider's writing has been published in *Cabinet Magazine, The Antioch Review, The Southampton Review, Artishock, NY Tyrant,* the online journal *3:AM Magazine,* and elsewhere. Her flash fiction story "Stutterers" was chosen by guest editor Amy Hempel for *Best Small Fictions 2017.* She lives in New York.

Ashlee Crews lives in Durham, North Carolina. Her stories have appeared in *McSweeney's, The Pushcart Prize, The Southern Review, The Southwest Review, Prairie Schooner,* and *Shenandoah.* She is currently working on a short story collection and a novel. In 2013, she received The Rona Jaffe Award.

Stuart Dischell is the author of *Good Hope Road,* a National Poetry Series Selection (Viking 1993), *Evenings & Avenues* (Penguin 1996), *Dig Safe* (Penguin 2003), *Backwards Days* (Penguin 2007), and *Children With Enemies* (University of Chicago Press, 2017), the pamphlets *Animate Earth* and *Touch Monkey,* and the chapbook *Standing on Z* (Unicorn Press, 2017). His poems have appeared in *The Atlantic, AGNI, The New Republic, Slate, Kenyon Review,* and anthologies including *Essential Poems, Hammer and Blaze, The Pushcart Prize,* and *Good Poems.* He is a recipient of awards from the NEA, the North Carolina Arts Council, and the John Simon Guggenheim Foundation.

Lee Clay Johnson is the author of the novel *Nitro Mountain* (Knopf, 2016), which won the 2017 Sue Kaufman Prize from the American Academy of Arts and Letters. His stories have appeared in numerous publications. He holds a BA from Bennington College and an MFA from the University of Virginia. He grew up around Nashville in a family of bluegrass musicians, and currently lives in New York City.

Randall Kenan teaches English and comparative literature at the University of North Carolina at Chapel Hill. His most recent nonfiction book is *The Fire This Time* (Melville, 2007). His collection of stories *Let the Dead Bury Their Dead* (Harcourt, 1992) was a finalist for the National Book Critics Circle Award. *Walking on Water* (Knopf, 1999) was nominated for the

Southern Book Award. Kenan has won many awards, including a Guggenheim Fellowship, a Whiting Writers Award, and the John Dos Passos Prize.

Louise Marburg is the author of a collection of stories, *The Truth About Me* (WTAW Press, 2017), which was named by the San Francisco Chronicle and *Entropy* as a best book of 2017, and is a Foreword Indie Finalist. Her work has appeared in *Narrative, The Pinch, Carolina Quarterly,* and elsewhere. She lives in New York City with her husband, the artist Charles Marburg. You can find her at louisemarburg.com.

Lydia Martín is an award-winning writer who spent more than two decades covering Miami's growth and cultural evolution for *The Miami Herald.* She won the Ploughshares Emerging Writer's Contest in 2016. Her writing has appeared in books such as *Presenting Celia Cruz* (Clarkson Potter, 2004); in literary journals such as *Fifth Wednesday Journal* and *Origins Literary Journal;* and in magazines such as *Billboard, Esquire, InStyle, Oprah, Latina Hispanic* and *Out.* She has an MFA in creative writing from Bennington College.

Bobbie Ann Mason published her first short stories in the *New Yorker* in the 1980s. Her story "Shiloh" and her novel *In Country* (Harper & Row, 1985) are taught widely in college classes. Her memoir, *Clear Springs* (Random House, 1999), was a finalist for the Pulitzer Prize. Her newest novel is *The Girl in the Blue Beret* (Random House, 2011). A retrospective collection of her works called *Patchwork: A Bobbie Ann Mason Reader,* with an introduction by George Saunders, is new this summer (University Press of Kentucky, 2018).

Dan McDermott received his MFA in creative writing and literature from the Bennington Writing Seminars. He has new fiction currently appearing in *The Southampton Review.*

Eileen Pollack is the author, most recently, of the novels *The Bible of Dirty Jokes* (Four Way, 2018) and *A Perfect Life* (Ecco, 2016). Eileen's work of creative nonfiction *Woman Walking Ahead* (University of New Mexico Press, 2002) is the basis for a recent movie starring Jessica Chastain. Her investigative memoir *The Only Woman in* the Room: Why Science Is Still a Boys' Club was published in 2015 by Beacon Press. Eileen's essay "Pigeons" was selected for the 2013 edition of Best American Essays. She is a professor on the faculty of the Helen Zell MFA Program in Creative Writing at the University of Michigan.

Ron Rash is the author of the 2009 PEN/Faulkner Finalist and New York Times bestselling novel Serena (HarperCollins, 2008), in addition to five other novels, including One Foot in Eden (Picador, 2003), Saints at the River (Picador, 2004), The World Made Straight (Picador, 2007), and Above the Waterfall (Ecco, 2015); five collections of poems; and six collections of stories, among them Burning Bright (Ecco, 2010), which won the 2010 Frank O'Connor International Short Story Award, Chemistry and Other Stories (Picador, 2007), which was a finalist for the 2007 PEN/Faulkner Award, and most recently, Something Rich and Strange (Ecco, 2014). Twice the recipient of the O. Henry Prize, he teaches at Western Carolina University.

Erin Singer grew up in the Yukon and Saskatchewan. She lives in Las Vegas.

Serene Taleb-Agha is a fiction and essay writer. Her current interests range through nature, artificial intelligence, gender dynamics, and American Muslim communities. She develops software by day and writes on weekends—two activities that are often very different but sometimes not. Serene lives north of Atlanta in the beautiful company of her husband and three children.

Su Tong (苏童) is one of China's most acclaimed fiction writers with a prolific oeuvre. His representative works include the novels Rice, My Life as Emperor (Faber and Faber, 2011), The Boat to Redemption (Overlook, 2011), the novella Raise the Red Lantern (Morrow, 1993) (adapted into the Oscar-nominated film of the same title by director Zhang Yimou), and the short story Mad Woman on the Bridge (Transworld Publishers, 2011). He was awarded the 2009 Man Asian Literary Prize and was a finalist for the 2011 Man Booker International Prize. His works have been translated into over a dozen languages, such as English, French, German, Italian, Swedish, Dutch, and Japanese.

Ting Wang discovered her passion for literary translation while studying American and British literature in mainland China. Her translations have appeared or are forthcoming in *Asymptote*, *Asian American Literary Review*, *Beltway Poetry Quarterly*, *Brooklyn Rail InTranslation*, *Denver Quarterly*, *The Iowa Review*, *The Massachusetts Review*, *Metamorphoses: A Journal of Literary Translation*, *Michigan Quarterly Review*, *Your Impossible Voice*, and elsewhere. She holds a PhD from the School of Communication at Northwestern University, and lives and works in the Washington metropolitan area.

GUEST EDITOR POLICY

Ploughshares is published four times a year: mixed issues of poetry and prose in the spring and winter, a prose issue in the summer, and a longform prose issue in the fall. The spring and summer issues are guest-edited by different writers of prominence, fall and winter issues are staff-edited. Guest editors are invited to solicit up to half of their issues, with the other half selected from unsolicited manuscripts screened for them by staff editors. This guest editor policy is designed to introduce readers to different literary circles and tastes, and to offer a fuller representation of the range and diversity of contemporary letters than would be possible with a single editorship. Yet, at the same time, we expect every issue to reflect our overall standards of literary excellence.

SUBMISSION POLICIES

We welcome unsolicited manuscripts from June 1 to January 15 (postmark dates). We also accept submissions online. Please see our website (pshares.org/submit) for more information and guidelines. All submissions postmarked from January 16 to May 31 will be recycled or returned unread. From March 1 to May 15, we accept submissions online for our Emerging Writer's Contest.

Our backlog is unpredictable, and staff editors ultimately have the responsibility of determining for which editor a work is most appropriate. If a manuscript is not timely for one issue, it will be considered for another. Unsolicited work sent directly to a guest editor's home or office will be ignored and discarded.

All mailed manuscripts and correspondence regarding submissions should be accompanied by a self-addressed, stamped envelope and email address. Expect three to five months for a decision. We now receive well over a thousand manuscripts a month.

For stories and essays that are significantly longer than 7,500 words, we are now accepting submissions for Ploughshares Solos, which will be published as e-books and collected in a longform prose issue in the fall. Pieces for this series, which can be either fiction or nonfiction, can stretch to novella length and range from 7,500 to 20,000 words. The series is edited by Ladette Randolph, Ploughshares Editor-in-chief.

Simultaneous submissions are amenable as long as they are indicated as such and we are notified immediately upon acceptance elsewhere. We do not reprint previously published work. Translations are welcome if permission has been granted. We cannot be responsible for delay, loss, or damage. Payment is upon publication: $45/printed page, $90 minimum and $450 maximum per author, with two copies of the issue and a one-year subscription. For Ploughshares Solos, payment is $450 for long stories and novellas. The prize for our Emerging Writer's Contest is $2,000 for the winner in each genre: fiction, poetry, and nonfiction.

Ploughshares greatly appreciates the support of its patrons. To give your tax-deductible contribution to the Ploughshares Endowed Fund, call us at (617) 824-3753 or visit www.pshares.org/engage/donate.

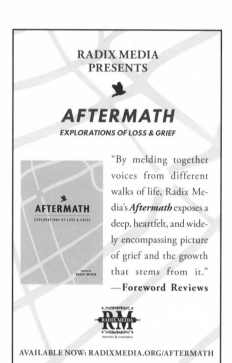
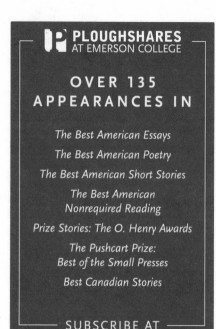